SHORT
DRIVE,
SWEET
CHARIOT

WILLIAM SAROYAN

SHORT DRIVE, SWEET CHARIOT

PHAEDRA 1966

Library of Congress Catalog Card
Number: 66-17957

First Edition, April 1, 1966

Phaedra Inc.
220 East 42nd Street
New York, N.Y. 10017

Short Drive, Sweet Chariot

This little book is for the big literary critic, the big literary agent, the big literary publisher, the big literary editor, the big literary public relations man, the big literary lawyer, the big literary movie producer, the big literary dentist, the big literary business man, and all of the other big literary bores, to whom this little book says two little famous literary words.

WILLIAM SAROYAN

70-150

In the summer of 1963 I bought a 1941 Lincoln limousine in New York, so that I might be chauffeur in California to the few remaining dignitaries in my family.

I enjoyed imagining them being serene and lordly in the back, telling me to take them to the country, to the muscat vineyards, the apricot orchards, the olive groves, and the fig gardens.

I also imagined picking up old hoboes along the highways and taking them wherever they wanted to go. I liked the idea of having them sit in a kind of chariot, and I planned to have for them cigars, whiskey, and crisp new money.

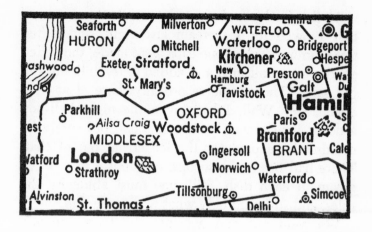

1. When I woke up Sunday morning in London, Ontario, after the long drive from Manhattan, and after four hours of sleep, my cousin John was writing a letter.

"To Mihr. Write something on the bottom."

I wrote: "Johnny and I will be at your house in six or seven days, and I want to take you for a drive in this limousine that's twenty-two years old."

The lifting of the Venetian blinds in the hotel room let in a lot of hot sunlight in which to gulp down hot coffee—and right there's the fun of driving across the country: hot sunlight, hot coffee, and the first hot cigarette of the day.

Before leaving the room, I gathered together the usual souvenirs: stationary, ashtray, small towel, and the *Don't Disturb* sign. If a Bible is in especially good condition, or falling to pieces, or marked up, I take that, too. Bible-stealing *is* stealing, of course, but I intend to make a generous donation to the Gideons some day (deductible).

11

At the Cashier's I wasted ten minutes insisting that I owed for ice cream last night, and coffee this morning. Telephone calls were made, the coffee charge was confirmed and added to the bill, but the girl said, "There is no record anywhere of any ice cream, sir." Well, I had given the night bell-boy a dollar for showing us to our room, but surely he couldn't have paid for the ice cream out of that. There had been four scoops, or about a pint of ice cream in each dish. Still, one must abide by the rules, and so I paid only what was on the bill.

We went out and got into the limousine and drove through town to Highway 2, on our way to Windsor, Detroit, and finally Ann Arbor, where we were expected around three in the afternoon.

There were less than two hundred miles to drive, so there was no hurry. I hoped to give a lift to an old Canadian hobo, but there wasn't one on Highway 2. At last, driving through Thamesville, I saw two boys standing in the shade of a great elm, hitching a ride. They weren't sure I actually wanted them to get into the car, so I said, "Get in." When they had settled themselves I put on the nearest thing I had to a chauffeur's cap, which I bought in Moscow for the equivalent of a dollar in 1960, turned around and said, "Where to?" I hoped they would say, "San Diego, please."

One of the boys said, "Chatham." I didn't understand what he meant, perhaps because his enunciation was soft, after the British manner, and the hearing in my right ear is poor, as it has been most of my life.

"What'd he say, Johnny?"

"I didn't hear him, either."

"How far is it, that place where you want to go?"

"About ten miles straight ahead."

"What's the name of the place again?"

"Chatham."

"Is that on the Triptik?" I asked my cousin.

"Chatham," he read. "Population 22,218. Trade center for a rich agricultural district. During the Civil War, this was the northern terminus of the Underground Railway, and there are may points of historic interest associated with those times."

"Chath-am, or Chat-ham?"

"Chat-ham," the older boy said, using the car lighter to light his cigarette, while the younger boy lighted his with a match.

I thought, "Easy on the matches and don't set fire to the upholstery." This thought perplexed me, but the next one was even more perplexing. "And don't steal my cousin's camera."

"*Where*, in Chatham?"

"Show," the older boy said, but again I wasn't sure I knew what he had said or what he meant. In the first place I hadn't heard that word in that context in thirty years or more, and with his particular enunciation, and with the word standing alone, it didn't sound like a word at all. He was obliged to say the word again, and then a third time, but I still didn't know what he was saying or what he meant, so my cousin said, "They're going to a movie."

"Is that right?"

"Yes," the younger boy said.

This struck me as being a very interesting state

of affairs, worth investigating, because here was this absolutely magnificent summer morning in Canada, and here were these two boys of Thamesville, more or less in some sort of Sunday clothes, and they had stood in the shade of a great tree to hitch a ride to Chatham, in order to go to a movie at high noon. They wanted to get out of the sun and into the movie. Now, why would two healthy Canadian boys, born and raised in a fine quiet village near streams and lakes want to do *that*, instead of going fishing, for instance, or instead of getting into a baseball game, or going for a hike, or a picnic, or sitting home and reading a book? Surely, I reasoned, their pilgrimage would become at least a little understandable if the movie happened to be something fantastically spectacular; and I presumed that it would be Cleopatra, a movie I haven't seen and never expect to, which nevertheless I have heard discussed, even by people of some taste.

"What's playing?"

The older boy, the boy who was always willing to speak first but never willing to speak clearly, said what I *presumed* were five or six words of English, but once again I had to let him know I hadn't quite heard him, whereupon he said the same five or six words in precisely the same way. I told him again that he wasn't coming through, but I placed the fault entirely upon myself, on account of my gimpy right ear. This time the younger boy spoke up, and so I heard *something*, at any rate. It sounded a lot like, "Ramrod, Son of Spread Eagle."

14

My impulse was to draw over to the shoulder of the highway and ask them to get out of the car.

"Why do you want to see that movie?"

Each of the boys murmured something, and then all there was was silence, and the inhaling and exhaling of cigarette smoke.

"Watch those ashes, please," I thought. "You boys are a disgrace to Canada, a country I may move to one day because two years ago when I drove in a little Red Racer from Montreal to Medicine Hat I fell in love with Canada: Ottawa, Pembroke, Mattawa, North Bay, Sudbury, Espanola, Blind River, Thessalon, Sault Ste. Marie, Pt. Mamainse, Wawa, Terrace Bay, Schreiber, Nipigon, Port Arthur, Ft. William, Kakabeka Falls, Upsala, Ignace, Dinorwic, Dryden, Vermillion Bay, Kenora, St. Boniface, Winnipeg, Portage La Prairie, Sidney, Brandon, Virden, Moosomin, Whitewood, Broadview, Indian Head, Regina, Moose Jaw, Chaplin, Herbert, Swift Current, Gull Lake, Medicine Hat, and then across the border into Montana, *around* Glacier Park by mistake, instead of *through* it, and west to Kalispell where at dusk I saw my little girl Lucy come running out of the Rek Hall of some kind of Ranch she was at for the second summer, to ride horses and fall in love with cowboys. This car was bought for failures, not movie-goers."

I fished for a cigarette, found the package empty, asked the boys if they had one to spare. Both of them held out their packs. I took a Players from the older boy's pack, thanked him, and at the same time noticed them both sharply for the first time.

Well, they were a little confused, that's all, but not by me, and not by the limousine. They were confused by their parents, and by all of the other things that start confusing a man from the minute he can distinguish one thing from another, driving him on a magnificent Sunday morning to a pitiful movie in a town fifteen miles down the road.

I thought I'd better try to get them to open up, even though they were soft-spoken and not easy to hear or understand, because I felt I ought to know more about them than the little I could guess, which I knew was inaccurate, but I couldn't think of a suitable question with which to get the ball rolling, by which I mean to say I really didn't feel that I had a right to ask them any question at all, other than the one I had already asked about where they wanted to go. They hadn't ever seemed especially comfortable in the car, but not on account of the car itself, although it *may* have been on account of me, after all, a rather strange-looking man with a big moustache and a very loud voice.

"I'll never see these boys again," I thought, "and so I'll never again have a chance to say anything to them that might just turn out to be, to have been, something of use to them. It's now or never. They need something from somebody before it's too late, something from a stranger preferably, and here I am a stranger, and I don't know what to say. Should I say, 'Look here, boys, it's all right. Even being stupid all your lives is all right. Being stupid is not being stupid at all, it's being brilliant, please try to remember that, and try to stay out in the light

16

and air a little more. You live a better movie every day than any movie ever made, but go to the movies, too, if something or other makes you think you ought to, because *then* you ought to. You've lived a little more than you otherwise would have when you go to the movies because something makes you think you ought to.' Should I? Hell no."

So this is what I actually said: "Do you sometimes visit Detroit?"

"Yes," they both said, but I knew it was yes only because yes never sounds like no; and that's all they said.

When the limousine stopped at a sign near the heart of Chatham the older boy said, "We'll get out here." While they were getting out, the horn of the car directly behind me sounded quickly twice, telling me to get on with it. My cousin's little square three-dollar camera had been on the back seat, but now it wasn't there.

"What happened to the camera?" The horn sounded *three* times this time.

The younger boy jumped back into the car and brought the camera out from the shelf just back of the seat. He handed it to my cousin, got out again, they both said thank you again, the younger boy shut the door, and I sent the car forward with a kind of leap.

"My question about the camera didn't imply that I was afraid they had swiped it, did it?"

"Well, the camera was certainly out of sight, at any rate. We could have looked for it for a long time and not found it. Why?"

"I have a feeling that maybe I was a little rude to the boys about needing to go to so much trouble to see a movie."

"No, you weren't rude. What they couldn't understand was the car itself, but I could see they were afraid to ask about it."

"I didn't get that impression. I got the impression they were unaware of the car—unaware of just about everything, if you want to know the truth, which kind of depressed me, I guess, because, hell, when I was fourteen or fifteen or whatever they were, I was aware of everything, *excessively* aware, I might say."

"They weren't talkers, but even if they had been, I don't believe they would have had anything to say worth hearing."

"Local stuff, and local stuff is *always* worth hearing. Possibly a little family stuff, and that's always worth hearing, too. Possibly even a little fantasy stuff, and that's *really* worth hearing. I mean the kind of stuff that might suggest why they are on their way to a movie at high noon."

"Girls. They go because they know girls will be there, and because inside the movie they will be near the girls, or beside them, on purpose, or by accident. Thirty years ago when I was sending stories to *Hairenik* in Boston, when *you* were, too, one of the stories was called *Love is Twenty-Five Cents*. This boy of thirteen saves up his pennies and nickels until he has a quarter, so he can go to a movie. One day he buys a ticket and goes in. The place is almost empty and pitch black. He sits down next to a girl by accident, and he's about to get up and move to another seat when he decides not to. If the girl doesn't believe *she* has got to move, why should he? So he begins to watch the movie, which she has been watching for some time. Their shoulders just barely touch now and then, and this little touch makes him feel, and maybe makes them *both* feel something, something like a possibility of love starting. Little by little as the stuff on the screen moves along this possibility for love between them grows. And it's really the most wonderful thing in their lives so far, and maybe in the whole world, *ever*. They're in love, and they haven't even seen one another's face. And they're something like the man and woman on the screen, Rudolph Valentino and Vilma Banky, or whoever it may have been, it doesn't matter about that, the thing that matters is that by mistake the boy sat down in an almost-empty theatre beside the girl who had been sitting alone, and love happened. It happened because the boy had saved up his pennies and nickels until he'd had a quarter and had then bought a ticket and had gone in. And there she was in there, the one girl in the whole world for him, waiting, and sure enough he sits down beside her, blind and unsure of where he is. By the time he's able to see that he's down front somewhere and that there aren't more than twenty other people in the whole theatre, and he and the girl are the only male and female sitting together, love has happened. There are other groups of two and three girls or two and three boys, but he and this girl are the only male and female sitting side by side. Their shoulders continue to touch now and then, but their knees don't, so they just sit and wait. And then the boy drops his hand to the arm-rest and another wonderful accident happens. *Her* hand is under his hand but she doesn't draw it away, so of course he lets his hand stay on top of her hand, and they go on watching the movie. They watch a man bend a woman backwards and hold her tight and kiss her, and then the girl moves her hand, so that the palm of it will be against the palm of the boy's hand, and this seems to be the most incredible event in the history of human beings. The girl gets her soft fingers to entwine with the boy's, and then after a moment she holds his hand very tight. They sit that way a long time, the movie ends, the girl draws her hand away, and after the newsreel she gets up and goes, and the boy just sits there."

"A good story. Did you *look* at the girl?"

"How did you know it was me?"

"Who *would* it be? Sam Mukhjian?"

"No, I didn't look at the girl, and I don't think she looked at me, either. I looked at the movie the whole time, and so did she. I was Rudolph Valentino and she was Vilma Banky. I never did get the hang of becoming a professional writer, though."

"As you may remember, I liked *The Thin Slice of Ham* so much I wrote to Edward J. O'Brien about it, hoping he'd put it into his Best Stories, and after he died I wrote to Martha Foley about *you*. That story is one of the best in American writing, in my opinion. I have never been able to forget it. About ten years ago I came upon it by accident while I was looking for a story of mine, also in

Hairenik, so I read it again, and it held up just fine."

"My writing lacks something. Maybe it's confidence."

"Try not to lack confidence."

"The time to have confidence is when you're fifteen. I'm fifty-one now."

"It's not too late, and in any case you may not have lacked confidence at all, you may have had too much, for instance, to notice, to be *willing* to notice, that the stuff wasn't as good as you could make it if you really wanted to. That story about those kids in the movie is a real good story."

"The minute the hitchhikers said they were going to a show, I knew they were going because they believed they might run into love there. I'm not really a writer, I guess, because if I was, what would I be doing working as a chemist for the Navy for almost thirty years?"

"You'd be earning a living. A lot of good writers have had to earn a living. Herman Melville, for instance, worked in a Custom House somewhere for years. My son says *Moby Dick* is one of the greatest books, ever. What's in the Triptik about Windsor?"

"Population 121,980, Fort Malden National Historic Park is 18 miles south at Amherstburg."

"Nothing about Windsor itself?"

"Only what I read."

"What about Detroit, just across the river from Windsor?"

"Population 1,670,144. Greatest automobile manufacturing city in the world. Detroit is the oldest city of any size west of the original seaboard colonies. Today an endless procession of ships passes the city, carrying the immense commerce of the Great Lakes. Wayne University and several other colleges are here. Points of interest include the Detroit Institute of Art, Belle Isle, and Zoological Park."

"There was a man called Dr. Walter Heil who years ago managed the De Young and the Legion of Honor Museums in San Francisco. One night at a party he introduced me to somebody he said he wasn't sure he *ought* to introduce me to, a pleasant-looking man of about fifty to my twenty-seven, a Turk named Agha Oglu. Well, he looked a lot like Mihran, as I told him, and of course we became friends, certainly at that party, and whenever I happened to see him again. Well, for a long time Agha Oglu had been curator of Islamic Art for the Detroit Institute of Art. Later, he died, although he may have committed suicide. He was a very sensitive man, very kind, very understanding, very much like Mihran. When I read that he had died, or had committed suicide, I forget which, I felt I had lost another member of the family."

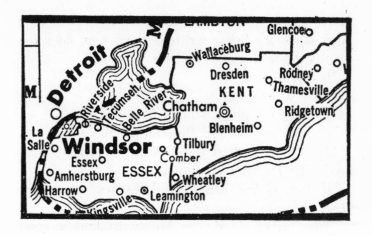

2. In getting from Windsor to Detroit there is a choice between a free tunnel and a toll bridge, which turned out to be a short ride for a dollar, which I mentioned to the toll-collector who said, "One of those things," impelling me to remark to my cousin, "Almost everything said by people one sees for only an instant is something like poetry. Precise, incisive, and just right, and the reason seems to be that there isn't *time* to talk prose. This suggests several things, the most important of which is probably that a writer ought not to permit himself to feel he has all the time in the world in which to write his story or play or novel. He ought to set himself a time-limit, and the shorter the better. And he ought to do a lot of other things while he is working within this time-limit, so that he will always be under pressure, in a hurry, and therefore have neither the inclination nor the time to be fussy, which is the worst thing that happens to a book while it's being written. Now, how does the Triptik guide us out of Detroit."

"Is *this* Detroit?"

"Why wouldn't it be?"

"I thought it might still be Windsor."

"But we just crossed the Detroit River."

My cousin opened the Detroit & Vicinity map inside the Triptik and studied it.

"If this is the Edsel Ford Expressway, we're O.K."

"They asked Marianne Moore to find a good name for the new car they wanted to put into the Ford family of cars, and she worked a long time at the job, considering what an automobile is, what driving an automobile is, what a highway is, what a carriage on wheels with people in it is, and all sorts of other things, and she suggested a nice variety of names for the new car, and then they decided to call it Edsel. I read about it in *The New Yorker*. She's a slender, beautiful lady who must be seventy, who nevertheless gives the impression that she's a little girl. I met her about twenty years ago for the first time at a party at E. E. Cummings' house on Patchen Place in New York, and then now and then I saw her at the cocktail and dinner parties of The National Institute of Arts and Letters, and I always got the same impression. If you were going to manufacture a new automobile would you call it John?"

"No, Valentino."

"I'd call it Junk. Remember the runaway horses in the streets of Fresno? Sometimes they would jump straight out of the traces and leave the people in the carriage safe and sound, but more often the carriage and the people went with the horse, and if there was a lady in there, she would be pale and silent, but if it was a farmer's wife you would hear a kind of banshee screaming. A free runaway horse was beautiful to behold, because this sudden failure of control in the animal had a kind of majesty in it, not unrelated to madness in men. But a runaway banging a carriage behind him was no fun at all to watch. Now and then the carriage would topple over, and the horse would be able to drag it only another ten or twenty feet, after which the horse would stop, trembling and dancing, or break out of the traces and go on. Horses meant something mysterious to me when I was a kid. They seemed to be part of a misplaced mythology. One evening at dusk a troop of drafted soldiers in uniform marched across the railroad tracks in front of the Rainier Brewery on M Street, followed by twenty or thirty soldiers leading unsaddled horses, giving me a sense of history, of man leading an animal in a campaign of force. Yes, this is the Edsel Ford Expressway all right, so what's next?"

"Straight ahead and it'll soon become Willow Run Expressway."

"And then?"

"Straight on to Ann Arbor."

"We'll stop at a gasoline station out there somewhere. I'll phone Bob Hodesh and he'll come and lead the way to his house. We're expected around three."

"It's three now."

"We're not far, and of course I'm moving straight ahead with the rest of the racing traffic. Four will be as good as three, most likely."

In an underpass I drew up behind a car that was going about thirty miles an hour instead of sixty, and I knew the driver was an old man, with perhaps his old wife sitting beside him. I am respectful of anybody driving a car, but I know that old men driving on expressways have got to be given *extra* respect because if they aren't an accident is liable to happen. We were in the second of four lanes, the swiftest of which was the first, which was the lane I wanted to take in order to pass the old man. I shot the limousine out toward the center of the first lane when a car going about eighty miles an hour suddenly arrived within a yard of the front of my car. Checking the intention of plunging out into the first lane totally, and drawing back behind the old man's car, meant jamming on the brakes suddenly and wobbling for three or four seconds, during which time it seemed as if I might not be able to keep the first-lane car from scraping my car. If it *did* in fact scrape it, it would very likely pile into the cement wall, and my car would bump about, possibly even leap or bounce, and then tip over.

My cousin was still studying the Triptik and apparently had no idea what was happening, what had just *happened,* or what *else* might happen now.

And then it was all O.K. A serious accident had been avoided.

"Take a good look at the car just ahead when I

pass, and let me know who's driving and who else is in it."

I tried to adjust the outside rearview mirror that was set into the frame of the front door, but the whole fixture was wobbly, so I had to duck in order to see what was out in the first lane. The inside rearview mirror was firmly set, but it couldn't reveal anything that wasn't almost directly behind the limousine, or far back. Two mechanics had worked on the door rearview mirror, but it was still useless. The car hadn't come with this rearview mirror, it had been attached by somebody, perhaps F.B.N.'s chauffeur, and it may have worked all right in 1941, but it wasn't working now at all. The initials F.B.N. were on both sides of the car, in neat silver.

After ducking and not seeing anything near in the first lane, I stuck my head a little out of the window and looked back. The nearest car, moving very swiftly, was about a hundred yards back, so I swung out to the first lane and raced past the old man's car, because there was always the chance that the old man would start moving out into the first lane too, very slowly, and wouldn't have the reflexes working by means of which to draw back in time to avoid a scraping and a crash. I shot a glance at the driver of the car, and laughed. He was a man of nineteen or twenty with his arm around a woman of fourteen or fifteen, and apparently both of them were fast asleep with their eyes wide open.

"Automobile lovers," John said.

"Yes, they probably *do* love automobiles as well as one another, but what you really mean is lovers in automobiles. What the hell are they doing on an expressway, though? They belong on a country road. A moment ago back there did you happen to notice or feel anything?"

"Like what?"

"Like a serious accident?"

"No. Why?"

"Well, through no fault of the lovers, and no fault of the racing car the accident would have been *with*, so to say, and no fault of the useless rearview mirror, and no fault of fate or heaven or the automobile industry, a very serious accident almost happened."

"Whose fault would it have been?"

"Mine, of course. I'm driving. While it was almost happening, for the fraction of a second involved in the earliest avoidance of it, and for the three or four seconds involved in the further avoidance of it, I thought, 'This is going to be very funny. Just as I am about to arrive in Ann Arbor, so the Ford Company publications people can have a look at the car, it's smashed, and now the only thing to look at is a great big heap of scraped, bent, broken, twisted American junk.' These expressways are great, but they're dangerous, too. The wonder of it is that more accidents don't happen, and I really know of nothing more deeply shocking than a serious automobile accident, because it is almost always something that could have been avoided, and certainly should have been. Its cause is speed, but the highways and the automobiles are designed *for* speed. Nothing is uglier than an accident. Driving a car is a beautiful thing that can always suddenly become an ugly thing. Accidents are dirty. D. H. Lawrence said some pretty interesting things about obscenity in a book once, but I don't believe he noticed that perhaps nothing is more really obscene than the accident, especially the deadly, or killing, automobile accident. When he was out in Taos for the sun, I'm sure he enjoyed riding in an automobile now and then, even though he wanted most of all to be a walking man, or at best a man riding a horse, but I wonder if he ever *drove* a car. There are men who are temperamentally unsuited to the driving of a car, and there are others who might easily train themselves to become suited to it but refuse to do so. For a number of years I refused to drive—the first two or three years after the publication of my first book, because driving would have imposed a kind of discipline on me that I believed wasn't useful to my purposes as a writer, and if I drove *without* that discipline, as I was sure I would be likely to do, I would kill myself, or what is worse somebody else. At that time I considered driving an acceptance of the possibility of suicide for me, and I knew I was opposed to suicide. I wanted to have an open-mind about it for the future, especially the remote future, but at that time I wanted to keep the possibility of suicide at a good safe distance, and I felt that that would be impossible if I started to drive, because in my writing the idea was to move out and take a chance. If I were driving, I would want to drive that way, too, which would be criminal. For twenty-two years this handsome automobile hasn't had a scratch, so not much more than twenty-two hours after I start driving it I almost make a wreck of it. *Almost,* though, for which I thank the writing on my forehead, as my grandmother Lucy used to put it."

"If you want to know the truth," my cousin said, "I was most worried about the first twenty-two *minutes.* I wasn't sure we would make it to the George Washington Bridge."

"Well, of course, neither was I, although I made a very special point of giving the car and myself and yourself a very good chance. As it was, you may remember I got confused on the approach to the bridge, took the wrong turn, stopped suddenly— stopping that way could have caused a serious accident—and then backed up far enough to straighten out and drive over the cement ridges to the approach, instead of taking the two minutes it would take to follow the wrong road down and around and to find the right road and come on back. Doing a thing wrong is something I so much dislike that it impels me to do three or four more wrong things, by way of correcting or redeeming the first wrong. I didn't want to take the wrong turn of the approach to the bridge because doing that would have meant to me that the whole drive would therefore be likely to have a pattern of wrong turns, of wrongness in general. Every man's got his own reasons for killing himself, which are probably based upon a kind of personal superstition he's come to live by."

"Like your theory about the writing on your forehead?"

"Yes. And his own reasons for *not* killing himself, too. His own reasons for avoiding suicide, although in avoiding, his reasons and his superstition, failing suddenly, may actually become the *cause* of the accident that kills him, at last. Well, it didn't happen back there a few minutes ago, and all I can say is I'm damned glad it didn't, because I want Bob Hodesh and the others to see this car the way it was in 1941, and here we are in the outskirts of Ann Arbor."

"Will we be going to the inskirts?"

"No, we'll just stop at this gas station, and phone."

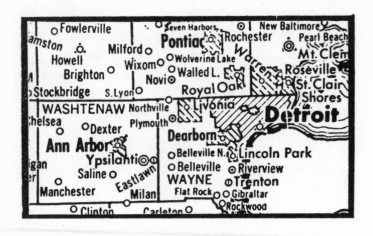

3. Across from the Ann Arbor gas station, near a cloverleaf of roads, was a Playland, with Ferris Wheel. I was on my way over there for a ride (it would have been the first in thirty years) when Hodesh arrived.

"Isn't this amazing? You were expected at three, and you phoned at *exactly* three."

"Wasn't it four?"

"You didn't set your watch back."

"Come and look at the car."

We went to the car, and I opened all four doors, so we could see the whole thing, in and out.

"Any trouble on the way?"

"During heavy rain in upper New York a little water leaked from somewhere onto my accelerator-foot. The motor seems to use a little more oil than it should. And I believe my cousin has jotted down a few questions to ask about a number of other things."

"What are they?"

"Well," John said, "there is sometimes a kind of rattle that seems to come from the speedometer when the car is coming to a stop. The hood seems to vibrate a little at high speeds. And I've made a note that it might be a good idea for an expert Lincoln mechanic to drive the car, listen to the motor, and then give it a quick check-up. Is that possible?"

"Well, do you know, actually there isn't a Lincoln expert any of us up at publications knows about, but even if we could find one, and I'm sure we could, I wonder if you would want to postpone your drive."

"No, we'll drive on, taking our chances."

"I'd say your chances are very good. I had really expected to see something a lot more vulnerable than this. After all, twenty-two years is a long time for any car, but this thing seems brand new. I can't believe the speedometer was set back, because if that had been a good idea from the point of view of the seller, he would have set it back to somewhere around 17,000 miles instead of 5,000. I'd say this car just hasn't been driven very much, but somehow has been kept in pretty good shape."

We drove to his house, and after a few minutes we were having coffee in the garden, near a grape arbor, with bunches of unripe grapes hanging down from the top.

"This is like Fresno. Will these grapes be Concords?"

"Yes," Mrs. H said, "but all we really care about is the idea, although the thing might be trimmed a little here and there." She seized a cane of the vine, hanging down from the top of the arbor, and was about to tear it away.

"Oh, no, don't make it neat and tidy. A vine ought to be permitted to get a little disheveled before pruning-time. That hanging cane is one of the nicest things I've ever seen, but then this whole garden is nice. Any frogs, gophers, lizards, or snakes?"

"We used to have a lot of things, but I'm afraid our cats caught them and brought them into the house for us to admire—lizards, gophers, and I'm sorry to say now and then a bird, too."

"Any bird who gets caught by a cat has forfeited his right to fly," John said.

"Who said that?"

"Well, I think *I* did. Why?"

"I thought maybe you were quoting Federico Fellini."

"Why should I quote him?"

"I mean, everybody's going to Fellini's movies these days. Have you seen any of them?"

"The first one," Annette said. "Or at any rate the most famous one."

"What did you think of it?"

"It was different."

"I saw it in Paris, in the original Italian, so to say, and I don't know whether that was an advantage or a disadvantage, because when I don't know what they're saying, I imagine that it's the greatest stuff it is possible for human beings to say to one another. I mean, I let the tone of voice and the manner of speech convey a meaning, or a *possible* meaning, and this invariably seems to be a rather large and worthwhile if slightly undefined meaning. Did they actually say meaningful things to one another?"

"Not especially," Hodesh said, "but it was an exciting film to see just the same. Do you go to a lot of movies?"

"Almost none. I went to that one because a friend of mine who is a pretty good writer and knows Fellini from having worked on a scenario with him told me I not only look like Fellini, but walk like him, and probably think like him, so of course I wanted to see what kind of a movie somebody like that would make. What I mean is, I am interested in who I am. A lot of stuff in the movie I could accept as having been stuff I might have done had I made the movie, but a lot of it I couldn't, and one of the things I couldn't accept is one of the best things in it. I mean, the suicide of the man who was happily married and loved his kids and his friends and hated nobody. If he had to do something crazy like that, in order to bring home the probable truth that in the end every man is unaccountable, I would have had him do something else."

"Like what?"

"Well, I haven't given the matter very much thought, but I'm sure that the unaccountability of man may be better and more truly demonstrated by something other than suicide."

"By murder?"

"Possibly, but not very likely."

"Theft?"

"Again possibly, but not very likely."

"I didn't see the movie," John said, "but I don't think I know what you mean."

"Is the movie showing anywhere in Ann Arbor?"

"Oh, no, it was here two years ago."

"Well, I'm afraid I can't ask my cousin to go and see it and come back, so we can continue this discussion. What I *might* have the man in the movie do instead of commit suicide is this, for instance: sit down late at night and write a letter to somebody, perhaps somebody in a position of world leadership, for instance, and then wake up his wife, or his son, or his daughter, and read the letter, all the while looking at the sleepy and confused face. And then look at the letter, and let it fall like a leaf from a tree into a wastebasket, or into a fire in a fireplace, and then go and put the listener back to sleep."

"It's not the same thing at all."

A few large drops of rain began to fall, so we went back into the house, expecting a heavy rain, but it never came, and soon it was evening, and friends began to arrive.

Clarence Dykeman brought a loaf of bread he himself had just baked. On three occasions during the rest of the drive I broke off a piece of it and ate it, without butter or cheese or anything else, because it was such good bread.

His wife Helda said, "Clarence loves to bake a couple of good loaves of bread now and then."

"I can understand that such a thing would be deeply satisfying."

"I have always enjoyed eating bread," Dykeman

said, "but I have seldom found bread I really liked, so I decided to bake my own."

"Bread and water is supposed to be punishment fare, but it's a lot less punishing than cake and ice cream, for instance. Too much dietary variety diverts the mind from what *should* be its full-time work."

"What's that?" John said.

"The full-time work of any mind should be to discover as complex a truth about itself as possible; and that's most likely to happen when the demands of the body are kept at minimum, although there have been fat men who have been vigorously concerned about man's total truth. Chesterton, for instance. But I have always been puzzled by the fact that Buddha was fat."

We talked through cocktails, through dinner, after dinner, and then we sang, and then we settled back and *really* began to talk, because after midnight talk takes off. We talked about everything, and then we said good night.

4. Six hours later we got back into the limousine, and began to drive out of Ann Arbor on 23, headed for 96.

"Lansing has 107,807 souls," my cousin read from the Triptik. "It owes its growth to a legislative prank that made it the state capital in 1847. R. E. Olds' construction of the car that bears his name augmented Lansing's rise as a prominent automotive center. Of interest are the State Capitol, containing the War Relic Museum, Lewis Cass Building, and the Michigan Historical Museum."

"We're not going to Lansing, but what *was* the prank?"

"It doesn't say, but here on the next page Lansing is listed again, and this time it says: 'Named Capital of Michigan in 1847, Lansing is best known for its automotive industries. R. E. Olds built and marketed the first automobile here in 1887.' What *could* the prank have been?"

"The building of the Oldsmobile in 1887? Could that be what they mean? Could such a thing be considered a prank? I mean, by history rather than by a wit? Olds certainly didn't do it as a mockery of bathtub manufacturers, for instance. In 1887 my father was eleven years old, in Bitlis. One day a Methodist Missionary rode a bicycle out of Bitlis into the nearby village of Gultik, and the peasants stoned him. They nearly killed the poor man because he was entangled in something they believed was devilish."

"A bicycle may not be as easy to accept as an automobile. If your father was eleven in 1887, how old was my father?"

"He was five or six years younger I think, although I'm not sure. I'm only sure he was younger. The arrival order of the children of Petrus and Hiripsime Saroyan was my father, Armenak; Martin Avakian's wife Pepron, which is probably a mispronouncing of Priaprion, which is possibly a Greek mythological name, possibly not; Levon of Sanger; Missak, your father; and Mihran, the man we are going to visit at his home in Fresno in six or seven days. I used to like visiting your father at his shoemaker's shop on Blackstone Avenue. He was a good man, quite earnest about everything, but a little on the melancholy side, wouldn't you say?"

"He was certainly a sad man when my mother died."

"Vartouhi. I went to her funeral, and I had never before been to one. I saw her in the casket, and I couldn't understand. Death, I mean."

"I don't suppose I was allowed there, was I?"

"I don't remember seeing you. I was nine, I guess, so you would have been five. She was a beautiful young woman I had heard chatting with my mother at our house on San Benito Avenue—very sensitive, very delicáte. My mother was terribly devoted to her, and concerned *about* her—I remember that. Her death in childbirth made my mother angry. 'A lovely girl dies bearing a child,' she said. 'An ugly woman who can't find a husband lives forever, eating three meals a day and going to the toilet four. Where is the justice of *that?*' Your infant sister struggled for a couple of weeks and then gave up, too."

"And then old Jarjo brought my father a new wife from Armenia," John said, "and so my father came to Mihran's where I had been living for eight or nine years, and he asked me to go home with him. I was thinking only the other night if it wouldn't have been better had I stayed with Mihran and his mother. I was thirteen or fourteen, and I liked it where I was. I *loved* it would be nearer the truth—I loved the house on Ventura Avenue, I loved the garden with the great old almond tree, the fig, peach, and apricot trees, the grape vines, and every Spring the garden of eggplants, tomatoes, cucumbers, bellpeppers, okra, squash, parsley, mint, watermelons, and cantaloupes. I loved my own room, my own great private room, which I had all to myself until somebody came over and spent a night, when I would move to the couch in the parlor—but what did I care, it was only for one night, or at the most two, or three. I loved the old lady's kitchen, overlooking the backyard. And the front-porch that traveled on two full sides of the house, the Ventura side and the Raisina Street side. I loved the lawn and rose bushes, and the cat who listened to nobody but the old lady. I loved the old lady—she was great, she was kind, she was wise, she talked *to me*. And I loved her son, Mihran, as if *he* were my father, or my big brother. When my father came to take me home, I really didn't like the idea. I don't know what happened. Do you think it would have been better if I had stayed where I really wanted to be? My whole life seemed to change when I went with my father. What do you think?"

"Let me put it this way: what you did is *always* what you should have done. It really isn't the thing done that matters, it's the usage made of it. If you haven't started using going home to your father's house when you really didn't want to, start now. No, you shouldn't have stayed with the old lady and Mihran, because you *didn't*. Regret is a killer. Better see about not needing to have it—about anything."

"Don't tell me *you* don't regret anything in *your* life."

"I don't. It happened to me, it's my life, it's all I have, what good would it do to regret it? I'm glad about the whole thing."

"You've been lucky."

"Not in the things that happened, but maybe luckier than most in my acceptance and cherishing of them. You did absolutely right when you went home with your father, even though you left your *real* home, even though you entered the house of a stranger, even though you left the light to go into the darkness, as I suspect you felt."

"That's *exactly* how I felt. I've got to find out how to look at the stuff in my life the way you have looked at the stuff in yours."

"*Not* to find out is to encourage, or even to invite, the end. We have only what we have, what we *have had*, we can't have what we don't have, what we haven't had, and so we are obliged to use what we have and have had. Get the knack of that as quickly as possible. I know you're thinking about your broken marriage, and I know you haven't spoken about it very much because it troubles you deeply. Don't regret your marriage, and don't regret that it's broken."

Psychiatry of one sort or another is what happens on a long drive. It has *got* to happen, even if the driver is alone. Memory unburdens itself to that side of himself which is the great listener, and every man *has* that side—he's *got* to have it. Part of the machinery in man, in the mystery of him, is this listening personality, this willing listener to everything. Until the arrival of Freud, every man's built-in listener was the only psychiatrist, and his help constituted the only effective practice of psychiatry. This listener has been given many names, several of them by Freud: super-ego, id, alter-ego, and so on. By Jung it has been called the collective memory.

Others, less expert, have thought of the great listener as God, which is also the truth, for the listener is in fact so difficult to accurately identify

42

that it is necessary to think of him, or of it, as God. Certainly the best healing is the healing which comes from God, or from the whole complex which is beyond comprehension. And there is surely nobody who at any time is entirely exempt from a need to be healed.

The Americans have found the healing of God in a variety of things, the most pleasant of which is probably automobile drives.

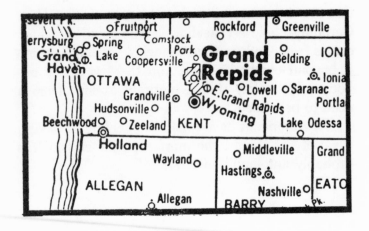

5. "I never expected Michigan to be so good to be in," John said.

"You're mainly in this limousine, and only incidentally in Michigan."

"I mean, whenever I've *thought* of Michigan—and I've never made a point of it—I've thought of the automobile industry, I haven't thought of a big green place, like this."

"*Big Two-Hearted River,* isn't *that* somewhere in Michigan?"

"I don't know, I didn't read Hemingway very much."

"They lived in Oak Park, Illinois, but they used to go somewhere north in Michigan every summer, and it was out of those visits that he wrote that story. I never read him very much, either, but I read some of his early stories, including *Big Two-Hearted River,* only I can't remember anything in *particular* about it, except that the boy's name was

44

Nick and there was an implication of sorrow about his involvement in the human experience. All of this country we're passing through was probably not unfamiliar to Hemingway fifty years ago when he was fifteen or sixteen. It's sweet country, I can see it meaning a lot to a boy like that."

"Did you know him?"

"Not then, but a long time afterwards I did, a little. We exchanged a couple of letters in 1935, for instance, and met in London, in 1944, and later in Paris."

"Well, he's dead now, so maybe you won't want to tell me about him."

"Why not?"

"Everybody dislikes being honest about anybody who's dead."

"I have *never* had anything especially unkind to think or say about him, even though he, in one of his letters to me, as well as in one of his published essays in Esquire, was happy to be unkind to a writer I hadn't at that time met, who turned out to be, when I *did* finally meet him six or seven years later, entirely unlike Hemingway's theory of him. Michael Arlen, that is, whose original name, as you may have heard, was Dikran Kuyumjian."

"What *was* Hemingway's theory about Michael Arlen?"

"That Michael Arlen—*another* Armenian writer, he asked me rather pointedly to remember—at his best had been a bad if popular writer, who soon enough stopped writing altogether in order to become a full-time playboy. I'm deliberately softening his terms, out of respect for him. I mean, Hemingway could get a little personal and mean about writers who weren't his equal, some of whom, including Michael Arlen, were not by any means otherwise his inferior. Let me put it this way: I didn't know Hemingway at all, actually, and I knew Michael Arlen enough to know Hemingway had known Michael Arlen a lot less than I had come to know Hemingway. And I think, when I finally met Hemingway, I resented his having attacked Michael Arlen in rebuking *me* for having kidded Hemingway about his preoccupation with bull-fighting. I didn't feel there was any need to drag Michael Arlen into it. As it turned out, Michael Arlen and I had nothing in common, as Armenians, or as writers. He was the son of well-to-do Bulgarian Armenians who had gone to Manchester when Mike had been about the age Hemingway had been as Nick in *Big Two-Hearted River*. I was the son of a Presbyterian preacher who had gone in 1905 from Bitlis to New York, to Paterson, and finally to Fresno. What we probably had in common was an easy toleration of one another's manners. I enjoyed Mike's rather crisp elegance, as I suspect he enjoyed my unawareness of the desirability of any kind of elegance at all. He was devoted to form in his daily life, while I had no time for it *there* at all, because of my eagerness to find it in art, or rather to find the kind of form in writing that would permit me to work."

"Did you ever find what you were looking for?"

"Well, if I didn't, I got three dozen books out of *trying*, at any rate. Actually, I suppose I didn't, at that. What I mean is I was too concerned about form in writing to care about trying for superficial form in my daily life. On the other hand, Mike went to quite a lot of trouble about dressing for lunch, let alone dinner. I had lunch at the Automat on beef pie for fifteen cents if I felt very hungry, and my idea of a classy dinner was a spread at a Chinese restaurant. What do you want to *know* about Hemingway?"

"A long time ago I read somewhere that his writing influenced your writing. Did it?"

"*The Boys in the Back Room,* by Edmund Wilson? If that's what you read, that was the *theory* all right, in 1938. Now, how can I say what I really believe about a thing like that, which is quite simply that I was *not* influenced by Hemingway at all, when my own son, at nineteen, reading Hemingway and reading me, believes I was? I love my son, and I respect his intelligence, so I try to guess what he means, in order to discover if that is true, that I *was* in fact influenced by Hemingway, and also perhaps at the same time to discover how and why this happened, but the whole theory falls to pieces the more I think about it."

"Who decides about a thing like that?"

"Edmund Wilson."

"Well, when you *read* Hemingway, did you *like* his writing?"

"Some of it I liked, but not more than I liked a lot of other writing I was reading at the same time. My best reading was from about the age of fifteen to about the age of twenty. After that, I was no longer a reader, I was a writer. I was fifteen in 1923, when Hemingway was still more or less unknown, and I was twenty in 1928. The writers I liked best and therefore *might* have been influenced by were George Bernard Shaw, H. L. Mencken, Sherwood Anderson, Eugene O'Neill, and a whole mob of writers whose stuff hasn't held up. For instance, I liked reading poetry, almost anybody's poetry, but especially Walt Whitman's, which has held up just fine. The arrival in my life of *The Spoon River Anthology* by Edgar Lee Masters, for instance, was an event I cannot permit myself to say was not important in 1923, no matter what I may think of that work in 1963. In 1923 I thought it was great. Well, three or four weeks ago I came upon a very handsome new edition of it in Scribner's on Fifth Avenue, and I began to read it from the top: title, year of copyright, slogan, so to put it, opening matter, first page, and so on. Well, just standing there, reading stuff free of charge, wham— it hit me again, almost as if I was on the night shift at Postal Telegraph in Fresno, where I did so much of my reading in those days, after eleven at night when there were no more telegrams to deliver, or at home, after work, at 3204 El Monte Way—crazy about writing in general, and eager to get along to my own, but still inept about the whole thing, still without my own language, my own way or style, my own usage of English, which is a very tough language to use effectively. Almost fifty-five years of age, and after forty years, *The Spoon River Anthology* still moved me deeply, although I now felt it fell short of being a great work. Well, what about *that? Was* my writing influenced by the fact that I had at fifteen been deeply moved by *The Spoon*

River Anthology—the writing I didn't even begin to do until almost ten years later, and didn't begin to publish until 1934? Who knows? Who can say? And what about the dozens of nameless and now forgotten poets whose poems I read in *Poetry,* along with the poems by the poets who turned out to be unforgettable? Ezra Pound, William Carlos Williams, Wallace Stevens. Might it not have been the very *existence* of poetry itself, in English, that really influenced my writing, even though in form my writing is prose? I really don't know, but my guess would be that it was. And the poetry was not necessarily great, if in fact it *ever* really was, or written by great poets. A lot of it was bad, by poets who never did live to write *one* good poem, let alone a great one. All the same, all of it had *that* vision, that excitement about living, about dying, about experiencing time, about aloneness."

"Then, why did he *say* that Hemingway influenced your writing?"

"Well, it was raining, and he didn't want to say a lot of other things, because if he did people might get the idea he didn't know how to write, and the first thing a writer has *got* to do is give the impression that he *does* know how to write. After that, anything he decides to say, or is compelled by his theme or theory to say, has got to look a lot like holy writ. And don't forget I'm talking about Edmund Wilson who is just about the best creative critic now writing in the English language. This *is* green country all right, and where Hemingway knew some wonderful times as a boy, but my writing was always all over the place, trying to get as

49

much of it as possible, from here, from there, and, if it would help matters at all, from nowhere, and swiftly, carelessly, adios muchacho, I never met you and never will, that's all the time I've got just now, take care of yourself. My writing was never in a straight line, but wait a minute, maybe it *was*, now and then. In my first book there is a story called *A Curved Line* that is in fact in a straight line, and my son Aram liked *that* story especially, and wrote to me about it, and the next time we met he *talked* about it. He may have been thinking of the writing in *A Curved Line* when he felt that Hemingway's writing had influenced mine. Well, I happen to remember *how* I came to write that story. The reason for its spare style, so to put it, was that I was *tired*. I was *really* tired from a lot of sporting life in San Francisco. I didn't want to *work*. I didn't want to *try*. I just wanted to sit at my table and use the kind of language that *couldn't* become hard to work with. It wasn't Hemingway's writing that had made the style spare, it was simply inevitable that the writing would be that way because the writer was too tired to write any other way, or to try for more. And I am not saying that that was the way Hemingway came to *his* style, although his writing *is* a style, perhaps the most successfully sustained style in all of American writing. What I'm saying is that if and when, as they say, any of my writing seemed to have within it even the faintest reverberation of Hemingway's writing, it was the consequence of tiredness in me and not of emulation of him. But wait a minute again, because the truth, or even a new *aspect* of it, is more important that having ideas come out even, and the truth is that I *did* name one of the stories in my first book *Big Valley Vineyard*, and that name is too near *Big Two-Hearted River* to be only an accident or a coincidence. Thus, there is at least *that* truth to bear in mind, even though the writing in *Big Valley Vineyard* is not anything at all like the writing in *Big Two-Hearted River*."

"Which of the two kinds of writing would you honestly say is the best?"

"Honestly, I would say mine is, dishonestly I would say his is, so you can see that not quite everybody dislikes being honest about somebody who's dead."

"Why is the writing in your *Big* story better than the writing in his *Big* story?"

"For one thing, I'm prejudiced. For another, his story is about a number of people who go fishing during a summer vacation, while mine is about working people who don't know what a vacation is. If they go fishing, it's to get some food at a time of unemployment and hunger. I probably sound as if I don't care for Hemingway's writing, or as if I'm jealous of his unique and extraordinary world-wide fame, don't I?"

"Yes, you do."

"I *thought* I probably did, which probably means I don't care for his writing and *am* jealous, but believe me there is actually a lot more to it than that, that's too simple; and what I'm really interested in, and have always been interested in, is that very difficult more that is inside of every truth, making it just a little unacceptable as an entirety. I really care a lot for his writing, and I am not at all jealous of his fame, although I don't care for it and am jealous, too. Is there a law written down somewhere covering that?"

"Yes, *your* law. Do you or don't you care for his writing? Are you or aren't you jealous?"

"Precisely. I am not fixed, as anybody in a work of writing tends to be, so why should I be willing to *write* of anybody as if he *is* fixed, or even as if he is fixable. Only death fixes, if you'll pardon the expression. Anybody who is the subject of writing is in *that* fact instantly alive and unfixable, even if he is *imagined,* or died long ago, so how can I possibly be willing to fix anybody, or the human race? I'm not death."

"Who *is?*"

"Hemingway, I guess, and of course we both know I really don't mean Hemingway. I'm only trying for that little edge of more that might in fact turn out to be useful. If you want to know the truth, when I heard in Paris of his death, I felt lonely for this country, I missed Michigan and I thought of him as a kid, as he'd been in *Big Two-Hearted River.* I missed a green time, a nation of sons, out in the green, out by the waters of summertime, not really *fishing* at all, but trying to find out a little something or other about the whole incredible thing. I didn't like him suddenly dead *anywhere* at all, in Idaho as it happened to be, early in the morning as it happened to be, probably up early still trying to find out what it is, what it really is, and not making it, but coming near, somehow coming a little nearer than it had

52

been until that moment. Out here as a boy with his father he probably came as near as he ever did to finding out, but when he went to his work-table and tried to remember in writing how it had been, how it had *probably* been, he *didn't* remember, *couldn't,* because there was too much to it, too much unspoken and unspeakable, too much felt but not really even felt, too much happening at the same time from all over the place and hardly any of it really about the green or the wet or the cool or the sweet of any of it, almost all of it about something else just over the edge of everything, different, hushed, true but in its very truth also false, unseizable, unknown, enormous, frightening, absolutely lovely, totally stupid and unusable, fierce and mocking, the very insects made of hardly more than heat and air speaking a tiny language of laughter, rage, torment, lust, and loss: he tried and failed, but out of failing got that style. I missed Michigan when I heard that the boy of *Big Two-Hearted River* was on the other side now, and I knew almost nothing about Michigan. I had been through a little of it by train or by car, and I had probably flown over some of it in an airline passenger plane, seeing the natural map of it far below, but I was out of it, it wasn't mine, I knew nothing about Michigan. Still, the first thing I thought of when I heard that he was gone was that he *had* been there the way all men are for a moment in *any* place in which suddenly for some unaccountable reason they must remain forever, in some kind of immortality, which nevertheless actually ended in the very instant in which it stated its

53

truth, flashing away in the flip. of a fin on the surface of water, making its sound and its ripple. And I missed that place, because once upon a time a writer had been there and had tried to remember it and had written about it as well as he knew how. Do you dig any of this?"

"Sure I dig it. I dig *all* of it. How did he talk?"

"Who?"

"Hemingway."

"Who's talking about Hemingway? I'm talking about the human race. Why do you say you dig something when you don't? He talked hearty like, I think you might say. But I also think you might say he did it only because there was a very deep courtesy in him that didn't permit him to have anybody else even *suspect* what he *knew*, but somehow hadn't ever been able to really get into his writing; because for one thing he had that style, and for another because what he knew simply wasn't possible to get into writing, because writing is writing. He never really said *anything*. You had to decide for yourself what he probably *wasn't* saying, and that's what made his name."

"How did Michael Arlen talk?"

"He talked the same way, only witty like. A wink was involved, although it was inconceivable that he would ever actually wink. He generally had an ice cold martini to sip as he went along, and there was a dryness of gin and cold laughter in his talk that was somehow warm, especially in the things you knew he wasn't saying, while you were being amused by the things he was saying. One time when I was fighting my life, as the Armenians say,

I phoned him where I believed he *might* be, at the Golden Horn when it was on 51st Street, and sure enough he *was* there. He came to a dark little bar on 58th Street where I was drinking, to see if there might be something to tell me that I could put to work in the fight, or something different *not* to tell me, an improved, or at any rate a more appropriate, order of an unspoken thing. He stayed longer than two hours of prime evening time, as we say these days, time he would have preferred to spend in a brighter place, a more fashionable place, among worldlier and more fashionable people, because he respected, perhaps even cherished, the grim, glum, dreary anger of an orphaned father, so to put it. I mention this because I gather that that's the kind of father you've been for a year—*out*, I mean. Well, Mike didn't really say anything, either, but he was *there*, and that's why I resented Hemingway's intention to belittle him. He was there because he was a friend, not because he happened to be an Armenian, or a writer, or a drinker. When we first met, in 1942, in the Bar at the Pierre, five or six years before the time I'm talking about, we *immediately* spoke in Armenian, and having done so, having gotten *that* out of the way, we almost never again spoke in Armenian, perhaps because if we had we might be drawing ourselves away from too many of our friends who didn't happen to know the language. He was there only because a friend who had been a laughing man had come to an unlaughing time. I'm sure he knew he could do me no good, but believed it didn't matter, he could at least hang around with me in much the same

manner that I was hanging around with my own useless self."

"Did he give you any advice?"

"Yes, he did, about where to get oysters on the half-shell—at the Grand Central Oyster Bar—and about two or three other things of that kind, but don't let that mean that I'm not ready to try to give you any advice I may feel I *have* to give, about *anything*. Just tell me your problem, and I'll try to find the advice you need."

"At the party last night you said that if you had made the famous movie that Fellini had made, you wouldn't have the man who was happily married, who loved his kids, commit suicide, you'd have him write a letter to a bigshot in the world, wake up one or another of the people he loves, read the letter out loud, drop it into the wastebasket, and then put the one he had wakened back to sleep. Well, I wanted to talk about *that*, but it started to rain and we moved inside, and while we were moving we began to talk about something else."

"And, just in time, too."

"Even so, I've been thinking about the whole thing, and what I want to know is this: what would the man write to the bigshot?"

"Well, let me see if I can guess. 'Dear Sir. Although we have never actually met, and although we are never likely to meet, and although, if the truth is told, I for my part have no desire that we meet, I was somewhat in an Italian movie not long ago in which it fell to my lot to kill myself. And even though it was only a movie, and a rather confused one at that, I really didn't want to kill myself.

And yet the scenario, carefully written by eleven clever writers, and rewritten by the director, a man named Federico Fellini—insisted that I had no choice in the matter, since I was a hired player who had for many weeks accepted excellent and excessive wages for work so easy as not to be work at all. In the movie I found myself to be a very decent sort of man who loves his beautiful wife and his beautiful children, but then *that's* to be expected, and is therefore not the thing that makes him decent at all, because who wouldn't love a beautiful wife and beautiful children? He loves other people, too, many of them not beautiful, some of them quite ugly, several of them downright sickening. Or if he doesn't love them, he also doesn't hate them, because he understands that they are who they are more or less by accident. I rather liked this decency in the man, and I thought that inasmuch as I am a professional actor in any case, why shouldn't I take his decency and make it my own. Such a thing is very easy for an actor. So I did, and immediately this created a terrible problem for me, for my beautiful wife, for my beautiful children, for the movie, for the eleven clever scenario writers, for Federico Fellini, for you, for your ugly wife and your ugly children, all of whom I love nevertheless, because I had taken possession of this invented decency in the man and had made it my own. I therefore decided that I would *not* kill myself, I would write a letter to you instead, and *read* it to my beautiful wife, as I am now doing, as you see, thereby improving the movie—not much, but a little, at any rate—and keeping my job, which

I don't need for the wages but for the decency. I am glad I solved the problem in this manner, and you needn't write and tell me that you are glad, too, I *know* you are, because you wouldn't be George and *not* be glad, and you *are* George. Yours truly.' What's next on the Triptik?"

"We're still coming to Grand Rapids, that's all."

6.

The day was Monday, July 22, 1963, the 203rd day of the year, with 162 days to follow. I watch the days. I watch the time. I have a built-in clock, the same as jockeys. I don't have to think about the time, but all of a sudden if I feel I ought to know the time, I know it.

"See if it's twenty-two minutes after two on your watch."

My cousin looked and said, "Twenty-*one*. How did you guess?"

"I didn't. I *know* the time. It started at birth, when everything else started, but it became sharp, or accurate, when I understood I was waiting."

"When did you understand *that?*"

"A little before I was three."

"What were you waiting *for?*"

"A variety of things which came to one thing—to live. Of course I *was* living, but I was waiting to live at home, to begin with, to get out of thàt place, the Fred Finch Orphanage in Oakland, as you know. To live with my father, and as you may also know he was dead. I was also waiting for my mother to come over to Oakland from San Francisco and take me home. I was also waiting for Christmas which is inevitable in the children of the western world. But what I'm getting to, as we leave Nunica on our way to Muskegon—better read about that— is that when I began to wait to live I really began to wait to die."

"Muskegon, 46,485, formerly known as the Lumber Queen of the World, largest city on the east bank of Lake Michigan. Today it is a manufacturing and resort center. How do you mean?"

"To live and to die is all there is, and they are always together, and not in a line of days and years, although we prefer the line theory of time, and probably should, because it keeps things simple. When I knew that in waiting to live I was waiting to die, the built-in clock began to tick. After that, any time I thought of the time I knew what it was. Twenty-six after two, for instance, on *your* watch."

"Is this related to E.S.P.?"

"Possibly, at least insofar as that unaccountable order of perception involves time, all time, past, present, and future, as the fortune-tellers who came to Fresno used to say in the streets."

"Are you always right?"

"Almost never."

"Then, what's this all about?"

"Driving from New York to Fresno in a 1941 Lincoln is what this is all about."

"I was listening respectfully, and believing."

"It was right of you to do that because I was telling the truth, but of course the truth is a very large thing, essentially inaccessible to us. I am almost never right about the time because when I went into the Army in 1942 I put a watch on my wrist and fell into the habit of glancing at it incessantly, so that I wouldn't be late to something or other. Until that time I hadn't wanted to notice the time with that kind of particularity, because instinct told me that watchtime, minute-and-hour time isn't really the order of time we are involved in. The order of time we really live and die by is another order entirely and has to do with the impact of the living creature—us, for instance—upon what we want. We want something, every one of us. In most of us it goes forever unnamed, unknown, undiscovered. It frequently seems to be other things: clothes, a reputation, a wife and family, a house, a car, money in the bank, and so on and so forth, but these things are only incidental things, so that so many people who appear to have everything actually feel they have nothing. As far as I am able to make out, the thing that is really wanted is a reality or a truth of self that is deeply meaningful and therefore satisfying, an order of self, that is, that is entire: incomplete, impossible to complete, flawed, vulnerable, sickly, fragmented, but *now*, also, right, acceptable, meaningful, useful, and a part of one larger entirety after another, into infinity. I doubt if this is a kind of wisdom. I suspect that it is probably a *system*, an action. Of course I'm almost never right about what time it is, as I'm almost never right about anything else, because in the matter of time-telling the watch on the wrist has diverted my skill, and in the matter of understanding, everything else we have that we cherish—art, religion, music, history, science, philosophy—has diverted my own need to find out for myself. Right now, for instance, I am trying to understand a continent, a system of highways, automobiles, drivers, passengers, this automobile, this driver, this passenger, and I am not making it, because it's all too clear, and this clarity, which is actually chaotic, diverts the action of discovery away from the total to the particular. There are too many numbers and signs along the highway. We know too well where we're going."

"I don't. Are we going north to Sault Ste. Marie, across to Canada, and west through Canada, as we decided in New York that we might? Or are we going to take a boat at Ludington and cross Lake Michigan to Milwaukee, or Manitowoc, or what?"

"Well, you see, we don't know. When we get to Ludington we'll see if there's a boat about to take off, and if there is, we'll take it and go where it's going. Another thing I don't understand is, what's happened to the hoboes and eccentrics along the highways of America I used to see so frequently twenty years ago?"

"Maybe they died, or maybe they gave up eccentricity and become insurance salesmen."

"Precisely. I want to pick up an old man and see if I can find out what he knows."

"What would he be *likely* to know?"

"I have an idea he would be likely to know about

time, since he moves on foot, and about waiting, since he is probably unaware that he *is* waiting. He would also be likely to know something about looking and finding, or not finding, but then these are all guesses. It depends on who the eccentric is."

"Are we sure he *will* be an eccentric?"

"I've used the word loosely; all the same, chances are he will be. Eccentricity is several things, and one of them is certainly going your own way, which these old men of twenty years ago appeared to be doing. Perhaps they did in fact reach their destinations. Let's stop at this stand and buy some of these black cherries from these kids."

The kids were a boy of eleven and his sister of nine. The cherries were in a cardboard box, and the price was a quarter. Their grandfather showed up from somewhere, and then their mother, his daughter, and then a girl of four holding a boy of one. Back of the stand on a counter there were jars of honey and maple-syrup, jugs of apple cider, and cloth-work of some kind, probably suitable for placing on a table. Each of us bought one of each, at a cost of around four dollars, which I was happy to notice made a pleasant excitement, of transaction, so to say, among all of them, and impelled the old man, in a manner that reminded me a little of Sherwood Anderson's father in *The Triumph of the Egg*, to wish to be somebody, rather suddenly, and to speak in a wordly manner.

"I think you'll both find these things all—a bag, Ella, a large bag—not *there*, baby, *under*, over there, the *white* bag. All fresh and—not *that* bag, baby, I wouldn't be able to get the jar of honey alone into that one. Excellent in quality. *That's* the bag. That's the order. My granddaughter."

"Ella is a very helpful child."

"Yes, she is. Seeds? I have packets of seeds here. Sweet William. Marjoram. Thyme. They're fifteen cents the packet."

"One of each for me, please."

"*Two* of each for me," John said.

"He's just lately separated from his family," I said, as if that explained two of each instead of one.

"One each for you, then," the grandfather said. "And two each for you. On the one, that's another forty-five cents. On the two, forty-five and forty-five—"

"Ninety," Ella said.

"Yes. My own seeds, taken fresh from my own— that small bag, now then, Ella. The one I said wouldn't do for a jar of honey. Where'd you put it, baby?"

The seeds were in letter envelopes, which the grandfather had sealed but not quite fully, because later I found little black seeds in my pockets, which for a while I couldn't identify.

"Don't bother to put mine in a bag. I'll just slip them into my pocket. I see you've written on this envelope Parsley. And a name. Is it yours? William Williams?"

"Yes, sir. William Williams. Seeds."

"Also honey, maple-syrup, apple cider, fresh cherries. And needle-work. What are *they* called?"

"Doilies."

"There is an American poet named William *Carlos* Williams."

The grandfather was confused by this remark. He appeared to be looking about among the words of his language for some sort of appropriate reply, and then he appeared to have despaired of finding them.

"He's a fine man," I said to my cousin, more of the grandfather than of the poet.

"What kind of a car is this?" the boy said.

"Lincoln."

"Anything else we might buy?"

"Just more of the same," the grandfather said, "if you want to."

"Another doily, then. That one there. Green, isn't it?"

"Yes, made by my daughter. Do you like doilies?"

"Yes, I do. They're useful."

"Under a plate, make an impressive—a little of that clean paper, Ella, right there, baby. This one's a dollar ten."

"Yes, sir. You've lived here for some time, have you?"

"What year is this Lincoln?" the boy said.

"All my life," the grandfather said.

"That's a 1941 Lincoln."

"Can I sit back of the wheel?"

"You get away from that car, Rob," the grandfather said. "These boys haven't got time for you to get behind the wheel and pretend you're driving."

"No, let Rob sit there, it's all right."

I opened the door and he got in and sat there and held the wheel. He was a fine boy who reminded me of my own boy when he had been eleven, who was now almost twenty, as Rob would suddenly be, too, with this summer day forgotten and grandfather gone.

"I don't suppose you know of somebody who wants to ride in this limousine to San Francisco."

"San Francisco?"

"Yes, sir."

"No, I don't."

"Me," Rob said. "I want to."

"Oh, Rob," the boy's mother smiled.

"He's welcome to come, if he has your permission."

"To San Francisco?" the grandfather said. "Now, what in the world would Rob *do* in San Francisco?"

"Rob, I don't believe you can make the trip just now," I said.

He got out of the car, sorry he couldn't make it, but awfully glad, too. His sister Ella poked him in the shoulder for having been so bold, and he said, "I'll get *me* one someday, and go."

I loved them, as I do all people at roadside stands, because they are always a family.

We drove on and began to eat the cherries. They were as big as bings, but the skin and flesh were harder and the flavor not so sweet.

"Eating cherries is a great thing."

"There's a lot of tartaric acid in them," my cousin said.

"Even so."

"No, tartaric acid's *good* for you."

"It doesn't have to be good for me. Eating cherries on a hot July afternoon in Michigan is one of the greatest things that can happen to anybody, and here it is right now—three minutes after three—happening to *me*, and to you."

"*Four* minutes after three."

"The seed of the cherry is something I like a lot."

-"To *eat?*"

"No, as a form, a displacement of space, a mass, a design. Isn't the tower of the Taj Mahal a cherry seed? Although, I suppose, if you *did* crack open a cherry seed with a small hammer you'd find something in there rather marvelous to behold and at least *interesting* to taste. Bitter, most likely. After the age of thirty, the bitter things seem a lot less bitter. Isn't it the Chinese, or is it the Japanese, who take the kernel of the peach seed and stick it at the center of an after-dinner cookie? Before thirty I removed the kernel and ate the cookie, but after thirty I ate the kernel and left the cookie."

"Isn't that an old man up ahead, walking?"

"Yes, I believe it is."

We drew up beside him and stopped. He was bearded, surely in his late seventies, his face creased and weathered, his eyes bright and boyish.

"Can we take you somewhere?"

He smiled, shook his head, and then saluted thanks just the same. I thought, "I'd give anything to talk to him, but nothing in the world can permit me even to *try*, because he doesn't want to talk." A smile, a nod, and away.

"He wasn't afraid of us, so why wouldn't he ride?" my cousin said.

"He's *there*, so there's no need for him to be taken anywhere else. He's all there, as you saw. In himself, as I'm sure you know I mean."

"And why didn't he speak?"

"I'm not sure, but it may be that when you are in fact *there*, it's belittling to speak."

"He would belittle *himself* by speaking, is that what you mean?"

"No of course not. He'd belittle that enormous *fact*, which by now to him is beyond speech, beyond language, unneedful of them, whole, total, right, and in any case he said it better with his eyes, his smile, and his salute."

"Suppose we see somebody else like him?"

"I don't believe I'll stop. It's embarrassing to intrude."

"Is it an intrusion to offer an old man a ride?"

"It is, although kindly intended. The impulse to do kindness has got to be carefully watched by whoever has the impulse. Kindness is tricky. Among themselves kids can manage kindness, but the fiercest kind of unkindness is equally easy for kids. When I first began to have money that hadn't been earned the hard way, I really wanted to give it to people who appeared to need a few dollars, and I did for six or seven years—kids, old men, tramps, beggars. And then all of a sudden I gave up the whole procedure."

"Why?"

"Well, I noticed that it made me feel good in a way that was embarrassing. I had no right to feel good at all, and I certainly didn't want to feel embarrassed. Back there at the grandfather's roadside stand it wasn't so bad because he *was* in business, he was selling stuff, and he did feel that he was doing a good job, he did feel that he had a feeling for business, a feeling for selling, because, he may have felt, traveling people suspected immediately that he was somebody who could give and take in worldly talk, somebody rather special, as of course he is, in any case. The small dealing in seeds, in *small* seeds, I might say, is what got me best, and most."

When we came to Ludington, it was just too early in the day to stop driving, and there was no boat for three hours, so we settled for a cup of coffee while the boys at a gasoline station filled the tank and added oil—so far the car was asking for a quart of oil every hundred miles—and cleaned the windshield.

My cousin said, "You told somebody at the party last night that Liston would knockout Patterson in their fight tonight in Las Vegas, but that you *hoped* Patterson would knockout Liston. Now, what do you think's going to happen?"

"It'll be on the radio around ten tonight, and if we're on a boat crossing Lake Michigan, we'll see if we can get it on the transistor. It ought to be an interesting event, but I don't see how anybody can imagine that it will be a fight."

"But what are you willing to *guess* is going to happen?"

"Liston will knock him out."

"When?"

"Unless, for some reason you and I can't even make a guess about, Liston permits the fight to go three or four rounds, he has got to knockout Patterson almost immediately."

"Why?"

"Patterson's neurotic, a superior man. There's very little animal in him. In Liston there's very little else. All kinds of writers are out in Las Vegas to cover the fight. Fight-covering is beginning to be a kind of literary event. This is something I haven't been able to figure out. Excepting of course the figuring out that one always does instantly about anything. A lot of writers haven't got anything to write about any more. But it's probably more as if they've decided their real writing is lonely and useless, and only those who are devoted to it are likely to be even a little interested, whereas in writing about something that everybody seems to be interested in, they can show-off their talents in a way that's more satisfying. It's kind of pathetic. None of the literary boys can write as well as the sports writers, in any case. A prizefight just isn't the enormity they seem compelled to pretend it is. But we'll grab the Frankfort boat at half past five, wash up, have supper, and go on deck and listen to the fight."

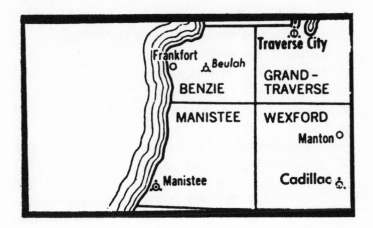

7.

Getting up to Frankfort on the east coast of Lake Michigan, after Ludington, the limousine cruised along easily at seventy miles an hour up Highway 31 to Manistoc, after which a detour put us onto Highway 22, which I would have preferred to take in any case since it moves near the water, to Onekama, and then winding up among hills lush with green—ferns and grasses of all kinds—the speed falling to as little as thirty miles an hour, the summer day moving into the quiet afternoon shade, with the smell of water blending with the smell of leaf, bark, earth, shade, and insect, the world was everlasting, and unbelievable.

There was nothing like the world. Being in it was beyond understanding, it was incomprehensible joy. The least I could do about it was light a cigarette and inhale deeply, inhale to the bottom of time, Lord, where do we go from here? How shall we leave it, how shall we ever leave it?

"How about the nut who sang, 'I would give a thousand tomorrows for just one yesterday?' "

"Caruso?" my cousin said.

"Not Caruso, he was Italian, *sang* Italian, and not McCormack, either. I don't mean the singer, in any case. I mean, how about the odd sentiment of that song? A thousand tomorrows for one *yesterday?* Twenty *billion* yesterdays for one good tick of time right now would be more like it, wouldn't it? *All* of the yesterdays, not for tomorrow, not even for today, but for this very instant, rolling the way this limousine is rolling, one little arriving-gone fluid instant of truth and trick right *now.*"

"Trick?"

"Of course, but it's a great trick—you think you're there, but you *were* there, and it isn't the rolling that carries you in and out of it instantly, all your life, it's the truth, and the trick, the great trick of time. This truth kills me, but the cigarette lifts me, dead, right back for a whole new start in life."

"What happens to people who *don't* smoke, as I don't?"

"They sit there and suffer in silence."

"Who says I'm suffering?

"The advertisement, which speaks the gospel."

"What advertisement?"

"The Sunday School one."

"There were *several,* according to what I remember from my Sunday School days at the First Armenian Presbyterian. 'Take up thy bed and walk?' Is that the one?"

"It's a good one all right, but not the one I'm talking about."

"Forty loaves, forty fishes, everybody ate, and was filled?"

"Another good one, but that's not it, either."

"Anybody here who is without guilt, pick up a stone and hit that girl in the mouth with it?"

"Try to speak English, but that's not it, either."

"Unless you are born again, you are dead ducks?"

"One of the best, but not the supreme one, not the right one, not the *only* one."

"I give up."

"Jesus wept."

"What's so special about *that* advertisement?"

"Wept. *Had* to. Overwhelmed by the hopelessness of man. Aware at last, only an instant too late, that it wasn't going to help, he was going to have come and gone as uselessly as anybody else, as if in fact he hadn't come and gone at all, or had been only lunatic, as so many before him had been, as so many after were to be. That's the one. Jesus wept, because death starts when life starts, and both move too swiftly for measurement, racing to a photo-finish dead-heat. Do you know, can you guess, how long ago these words were spoken?"

"Six seconds ago."

"Precisely. Six seconds ago last year, last century. Flash, bam, alakazam—belted out by Betty Hutton. And what do you know? There's *love*."

"Who's Betty Hutton?"

"The girl who belted out flash, bam, alakazam, that's who. My daughter Lucy's favorite television show was about Annie Oakley for a couple of years when she was very little, so when they made a movie called *Annie Oakley,* I took her to see it, and that's when I saw beautiful Betty Hutton, and remembered that she was the wild child who had belted out that variation of holy writ on a phonograph record. Some of our greatest people are scarcely known, but even when they *are* known, almost invariably there is a misconception about why they deserve to be known. Betty wasn't a singer or an actress, she was a demonstration of a force of nature, as a salmon getting upstream to spawn is."

"I don't believe I've even *heard* of her."

"There are people in America who, when they are asked, 'Who is William Shakespeare?' reply, 'Does he live in these parts?' You're one of those people."

"I've heard of the singers who have been on The Voice of Firestone."

"Well, that's not bad, but it's not enough, they never asked Betty onto The Voice of Firestone. While it was still on radio, though, they asked Gladys Swarthout, and when she sang the opening and closing songs, written by Mrs. Firestone herself—that means she was a Firestone by marriage—Jesus wept again. When Gladys sang, 'If I could tell you of my devotion,' Jesus just naturally up and wept all over again, because Gladys wasn't just another singer, although unlike Betty she *was* concert-trained, she was another demonstration of love as a force of nature, of love as *the* force of nature, the *only* force of nature."

"Love is a killer."

"Indeed it is, the truest, deadliest killer of them all, and since one or another of the killers mus' make the stab that stops, why shouldn't it be the best? Harvey Firestone and Henry Ford frequently met and sat and talked."

"I don't understand."

"If the world were vaudeville, Ford and Firestone would get top billing at the Palace."

"I still don't understand."

"You have this feeling that you *ought* to understand, is that it?"

"We were talking about how love is a killer, and then all of a sudden you said Harvey Firestone and Henry Ford frequently met and sat and talked. What I don't understand is how they got into the act."

"They're both dead, if you've got to have it spelled out. They were both killed by love. H. F., Henry Ford. H. F., Harvey Firestone. Henry, Harvey. Ford, Firestone. 'If I could tell you,' Gladys Swarthout used to sing on the Voice of Firestone, singing to Henry Ford, and to Harvey Firestone, and to their kids, and the kids of their kids: *If*. They're both dead, and some of their kids are dead, too, and Gladys isn't singing *if* any more, somebody else is, I could tell you of my devotion, somebody else is singing it now."

"They've taken it off. The Voice of Firestone isn't on television any more."

"Is it on radio?"

"It's off radio, too."

"There's your answer."

All of a sudden we're stopped by a flagman where two enormous bulldozers and a dozen trucks are involved in the making of a quarter of a mile of new highway. Well, at any rate we're first in line, waiting for the three dozen cars coming from the opposite direction to make their dust and begone, using an outside lane of packed earth while one of the bulldozers pushes tons of dry, soft, powdery brown earth on two inside lanes. Only a mile or two beyond this point is our boat, as I confirmed by telephone from Ludington, and it's due to sail in ten minutes. Well, I don't like to miss a boat, or a bus, or a train, or a plane, and so I want to take off as soon as the flagman gives me the sign.

When he *gives* me the sign, however, the second bulldozer is standing idle in the outside lane, over which only a moment ago the last of three dozen cars has come, and the bulldozer which had been at work on the two inside lanes is now gone.

The flagman waves, a bulldozer is in the outside lane, there is no bulldozer in either of the two inside lanes, so I presume I am to take the outermost of the the two inside lanes. A lot of drivers in cars behind me are waiting for me to take off, and so I do, swiftly and with all of the easy power of the limousine, as my cousin shouts, "Not that road, that's too soft."

But what does he know, he's never heard of Betty Hutton. About ten yards of rolling and the movement of the limousine is arrested. I shift to low and plunge forward two yards and down two. I then shift to reverse, nothing happens, and I'm stuck.

In the meantime the bulldozer in the outside lane has withdrawn, and all of the other cars in the line are rolling easily on their way, the people in them watching me and my cousin as we get out of the limousine to study the situation.

The car is stuck.

It cannot get out under its own power. We'll have to phone A.A.A. to send a tow-car to tow us out, and that means we've missed the boat, we've missed dinner on the boat, we've missed hearing the Las Vegas fight on the radio at ten, while the boat sails across Lake Michigan.

And all because of my swiftness, my plunging ahead, whichever way appears to be the only way.

"You were right."

"I couldn't understand *why* you were taking the soft lane."

"The bulldozer was standing in the other lane, less than twenty yards away. I thought the flagman wanted me to take the lane I took."

"There's no film in my camera, either."

"If there were, would your *camera* take us the rest of the way?"

"No, but it *would* take a picture of you looking like a damn fool. I'll go phone."

"No, wait a minute, maybe one of these bull-dozers can shove me free."

At that moment the bulldozer that had been pushing the soft brown earth swung around back onto the earth about twenty yards directly in front of the limousine and began to race straight ahead, the young redheaded driver standing, waving, and aiming the great blade at the limousine's front bumper.

I jumped back into the car, shifted to neutral, and got set. The driver of the bulldozer set the blade ever so gently upon the bumper, and then at a signal from me shoved the limousine out of the deep soft earth and back onto the hard, and away he went, waving.

We drove on, and reached the loading pier three full minutes before our boat was scheduled to sail, but the man in the office said there wasn't room on the boat for another car. I told him I had been assured by somebody on the telephone that if I hurried up from Ludington I could sail my car and myself *with* the boat across Lake Michigan.

He then said perhaps something might be worked out, but he couldn't guarantee anything. Would I wait?

I would. When did he imagine the boat would be likely to sail?

As soon as possible, but surely not for fifteen minutes, at least.

This permitted me to study the bumper, to see if anything had happened to it, or to any other front part of the car, when the bulldozer had pushed it free as if the whole two and a half tons of weight had been no more than a couple of hundred pounds. Well, everything *seemed* all right, except that there was a little something the matter with the bumper, although I wasn't able to decide what it was: there was some kind of imbalance in the design. On the right side there was a piece of metal crossing the bumper vertically, but on the left side there wasn't this piece. The thing had come loose and fallen under the power and weight of the bulldozer's pressure.

"I'm going back to get it," I told my cousin. "You keep after the man."

"You'll never find it, it's been covered by tons of earth by now."

"I've *got* to find out."

When I got back to where the bulldozers were working the redheaded driver swung around again, stood up, waved, brought up the machine, got down, and handed me the piece of metal.

"I'll never be able to thank you enough. What's your name?"

"Ed," he said. "I *figured* you'd be back for it."

I raced back to the pier, and my cousin said, "It's O.K. They've made room."

In fifteen minutes we were sailing. In fifteen more we had paid for our passage and for a cabin, since we would be sailing for around six hours and might want to take a nap. Inside the cabin, washing, and then sprawling out on the lower bunk, all I could feel was great, like flash, bam, alakazam.

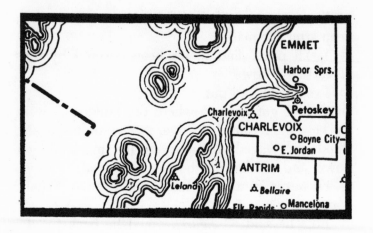

8.

There's something about catching a boat.

Something satisfying.

You made it.

It seemed as if you might not. It is always easy not to make it, to see the boat sailing away without you.

The picture is a bitter one in your heart, as if you hadn't gotten born, almost. As if you were going to get born, and then didn't, somebody else did, a lot of other people did, but you didn't, you were left back, you didn't make it, you were nowhere.

It is a sweet thing to catch a boat. It is success in its purest, simplest, and perhaps most supreme form. It is deeply satisfying. You have latched onto something. This something is the boat itself, but it is something else, too. It is one of the best latchings-on there is, for it is really a latching-onto time, action, schedule, and departure impelling arrival.

When you have caught a boat, you have left. You can stand on the deck and *see* that you have. There it is, where you were, and you're not there any more. You can almost see yourself no longer there, and it is much better, everything is much better now, because you have left, you are being moved away farther and farther from there, from that place, and you yourself are standing still, you are only standing there on the aft-deck looking where you had been, where you would be had you not made it, but you did, it was close, it seemed as if you weren't going to make it, and then you did, you made it, you became a passenger.

I stood and looked and saw, and I felt that that must have been how it had been when I had been born, and that earliest latching-on pleased me deeply, too.

The name of the boat was Ann Arbor No. 7. It was heavy with a full load of freight cars and automobiles. And there were about a hundred men, women, and children on board. The Cabin was No. 5, for a total cost of $19.50—car, cabin, my cousin, and myself, moving across the water about a hundred miles in six hours from Frankfort to Menominee, one of the great bargains of the world. The fore and aft decks were small, but there was room for everybody. The dining-room had only eight four-place tables, and two were reserved for the crew.

The supper was plain, but not bad for $1.85— for myself, apple cider, baked ham with applesauce, apple pie and coffee. American food, bad American food, but as I had caught the boat, and as I had stood on the aft-deck and looked where I had left, where I almost had *not* left, and as I had washed in the cabin—there was no shower anywhere on the boat, except for the crew—and as I had changed my shirt, and had sprawled out upon the lower bunk and had shut my eyes for ten minutes, not sleeping but feeling the action of the boat in moving, feeling success, and the grand condition of being a passenger, the bad American food was good.

Six slices of brown bread were heavily smeared with soft butter and wrapped in paper napkins.

"What's *that?*"

"Always take from a table anything served that you don't want at the time because later on you may want it."

"Do you want me to butter my six slices?"

"In tennis, anticipation is the difference between winning and losing. When I played tennis on the courts of Golden Gate Park in San Francisco I studied the matter of anticipation, first in tennis of course, and then in everything else. I discovered that bread and butter, or bread and cheese, or jelly, or jam, or honey, or anything else furnished with a fixed-price meal along with stuff that I really wanted at the time, should be taken from the table and kept in a convenient place against the time when the stuff would be needed. And when it became needed, generally two or three days later, it tasted good, and I felt I had scored another point in the game. Two or three o'clock in the morning, as a rule, with cold water, quietude, and anticipation of tomorrow. Whenever I returned the ball to my opponent, I anticipated where he would return it to me, and I was there, not waiting, but moving in, so that this time I could kill it. It made me feel good. I learned a lot in tennis, as I said in the story in which I kidded Hemingway about his fascination with bullfighting. For instance, I had a three-dollar racket with loose and broken gut, with which a drive was impossible, so I had to find out how to make that inferior racket win for me. I soon learned that it was an excellent instrument with which to cut the ball, and so instead of driving back a drive, I chopped it down, cut it, so that it went spinning just an inch or two above the net, dropped suddenly, and then bounced in a lopsided manner my opponent couldn't cope with, even if anticipation had brought him in position to make a return. I remember a young fellow who now and then was my opponent, from Austria, by profession a lapidarist, who whenever one of my cuts bounced lopsided directly in front of him, cried out with exasperation and admiration, 'Again you do this, again I am fooled.' Always butter your six slices of bread and take them with you, wherever you're going."

"Can I finish eating this one slice?"

"What are you eating *bread* for?"

"Well, it's wholewheat and I like wholewheat."

"You're not anticipating. You're trying to drive with a racket that's suitable only for cutting."

"Well, I'll just eat this one slice, butter the four, and leave the fifth."

"Take the fifth, too. It may be the winning point."

"Take it *unbuttered?*"

"Cut it in half, and butter each half. There's more than a quarter of a pound of butter for each of us. Any butter left over, put it on the stringbeans, they're good for you. You're in the game to *win*, I presume."

"Well, I don't mind winning, but I'm really in the game because it's the only game in town."

"Anticipate, make a point, run up a score, win, butter the bread, and take it with you."

"You've used my paper napkin, the only thing I have is this cloth one."

"Wrap your bread in the cloth one."

"It belongs to the boat."

"Take it, they almost didn't let us on."

"I don't want to steal their napkin."

"Have in mind mailing it back. During the game nothing's dirty. After you've won, nobody says, 'He did it by stealing.' Show me one American millionaire who made it by stealing napkins, and I'll ask you to *leave* the napkin."

"Will you ask me to leave the butter and bread, too?"

"Nobody got to be an American millionaire anticipating the late-night famine on the deserted highway across Wisconsin."

"We're not driving all night, are we?"

"We're driving, period. At any moment it can become all night. I ran out of gas one time in Virginia at one in the morning and nobody would stop because my cousin Ross and I, in our long black overcoats, looked like gangsters. One hour, two hours, and there wasn't anything in the car to make the stop pleasant—nothing to drink, nothing to eat, only six or seven cigarettes each, and one stick of Wrigley's Doublemint chewing gum. We talked about Jack London's story *To Make a Fire,* and we tried to make one, but it went out."

"What did you do?"

"Calisthenics, and talked and sang and made dogs bark, dogs miles away heard us and barked in that dismal way dogs have late at night in far-away places when the weather's bitterly cold."

"Dirty dogs."

"No, we loved the dogs, they were *with* us, they knew something was wrong somewhere in the night."

"What did you sing?"

"Songs from the play I had transformed from a fiasco flop in New Haven to a hilarious hit on Broadway."

"The play that got the prizes?"

"The 1939 play. 'Let the lower lights be burning, send a gleam across the wave. Some poor fainting, struggling seaman you may rescue, you may save.' And Number Seven on the jukebox in the saloon—the Missouri Waltz. In Armenian. We sang in comic Armenian, however, because nobody would stop and give us a lift to the next town. It was five or ten minutes between cars going in either direction and every one of them speeded up when they saw us. We scared a lot of people on that highway that night."

"And you feel that if you had had six pieces of buttered bread, all would have been well?"

"People in cars on a highway don't tend to be frightened of people on a roadside picnic. Had we been eating buttered sandwiches, somebody would have stopped."

"Why?"

"To be neighborly. As it was, three young drunks finally stopped anyhow, although we had been there three hours, and were half-frozen."

"How long were you *actually* there?"

"It seemed like *longer* than three hours."

"You're interested in time. How long were you *actually* there?"

"An hour and twenty-two minutes, but every minute was a *long* minute, and I'll never forget those three young drunks, the noise and laughter of them. We'll drive as long as the driving's good—it's one of those good clear nights when not to drive has *got* to be sinful."

"O.K., then, I'll wrap the buttered bread in the napkin and have in mind mailing it back."

"Anticipate, score, win—you'll never regret it."

"Don't anticipate, don't score, don't win—and you'll never regret *that*, either. I'm having a great time, that's all I can say. I'm seeing the country, and remembering and remembering."

"Was your childhood happy?"

"No. Why?"

"Well, you were smiling, and if you happened to be remembering your childhood, I would have imagined from the fact that you *were* smiling that your childhood had been happy."

"I was remembering the much more recent past of two hours ago."

"Did something memorable happen two hours ago?"

"Very."

"What was it?"

"I'll never forget how swiftly, how smartly, how confidently you sent the limousine knee deep into soft dirt, and then quickly shifted to low and plunged it two feet ahead and a foot deeper, and then shifted to reverse and rocked the limousine back and forth and made a lot of dust, and then shut off the motor and got out."

"I make mistakes."

"You make them as if they're *not* mistakes, though."

"I make them swiftly and efficiently, if that's what you mean. The whole thing took only eleven seconds. Another man would have needed two full minutes to get that stuck."

"Yes, it was a perfect demonstration of how to do the wrong thing the right way."

"I'm taking this drive across the country precisely in order to find out about these things. I went back and got the piece that the bulldozer had broken off the bumper, didn't I? I caught the boat, didn't I? We're sitting here eating, aren't we? In the dining room of Ann Arbor No. 7 on Lake Michigan, aren't we? I'm cutting the ball back to the tennis player on the other side of the net, so it bounces lopsided and leaves him standing there with his mouth open, ain't I? I've got six slices of buttered bread wrapped in paper napkins in my coat pocket, haven't I? Christ, I wish my father could see me now."

"Well, his kid brother Mihran is waiting for us in Fresno, and at least *he'll* be seeing you pretty soon."

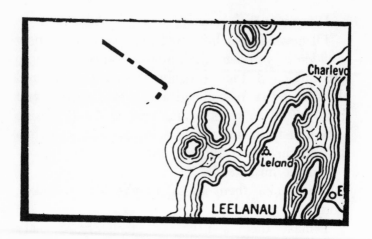

9.

When I was fifteen and had quit school forever, I went to work on a vineyard near Sanger with a number of Mexicans, one of whom was only a year or two older than myself, an earnest boy named Felipe. One gray, dismal, cold, dreary day in January, while we were pruning muscat vines, I said to this boy, simply in order to be talking, "If you had your wish, Felipe, what would you want to be? A doctor, a farmer, a singer, a painter, a matador, or what?"

Felipe thought a moment, and then he said, "Passenger."

This was exciting to hear, and definitely something to talk about at some length, which we did.

He wanted to be a passenger on anything that was going anywhere, but most of all on a ship.

On deck after supper I remembered Felipe's land-locked longing to be a passenger on a ship, and it made me feel lucky, because I had made it, and I wasn't sure he had. And angry, in case he hadn't, in case he was still land-locked somewhere, still not a passenger. Why should a few of us have all the luck, and everybody else, by the millions, have none at all?

My cousin came over with the transister radio to his ear.

"Singing," he said.

"Popular, classical, or semi-classical?"

"Something about a kangaroo."

"Hold him down, Joe?"

"Do you *know* the song?"

"No, but I like it, the *idea* of it, of a kangaroo being held down by Joe, while this other fellow, possibly the owner of the animal, asks Joe to hold him down. It makes a pleasant picture. I like all Australian songs."

"They're not singing any more. I think the song's ended."

"Try another station. Maybe they'll be singing it, too. I had that happen to me one time in 1941— *New San Antonio Rose*."

"This is the only station I can get, and now I can't get this one, even."

A man with two small freckle-faced boys walking beside him came along, and in the man's hand was a transistor radio from which the music of an orchestra was coming with an excellent quality of sound.

"Find out what he's dialed to."

The man himself said, "I think I've got Chicago, around 900 on the dial."

My cousin dialed to around 900, but got nothing.

"Are you planning to listen to the fight?"

"Oh yes, that's why I'm trying it out, now. This is the best reception I've had so far."

"You didn't by any chance hear a song about a kangaroo, did you?"

"No, I didn't."

"I *know* the song," the biggest of the two boys said. "Hold him down, Joe."

"Yes, that's the one. My cousin just had it on the radio, but lost it, and we've been trying to get it back. What's he want Joe to hold the Kangaroo down for?"

"So he won't get away," the boy laughed, while his father glanced at him with admiration, and perhaps a little surprise.

"Here's the fight," he said, and immediately a lot of people gathered around to listen.

For half an hour old prizefighters and famous people who had gone to Las Vegas were introduced in the ring, speeches were made, patriotic songs were sung, and then at last the gong was sounded.

Floyd Patterson came out of one corner, and Sonny Liston came out of the other.

After less than three minutes Floyd Patterson was out, the writers had seen what they had waited so long to see, and the Ann Arbor No. 7 came in sight of land.

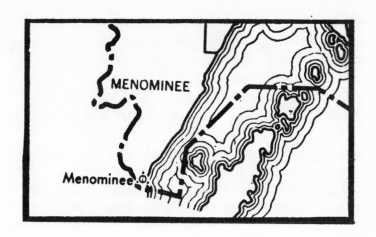

10.

There was a man and his wife and their three daughters on the deck of Ann Arbor No. 7 on Lake Michigan, and this man was a St. Louis Police Department psychologist.

His wife's sister, when she had been married to a man at the University of Florida, had exchanged a number of letters with me about the publication of a book of reproductions of Fletcher Martin's paintings, to which I had written an introduction.

While my cousin and I had been sitting on the sofa outside the dining room waiting for permission to enter and eat, while we had sat beside the wife and the middle daughter, I got the impression that I knew her, so I turned and smiled, and she said hello and we began to talk.

I told her I had only lately seen Fletcher Martin's one-man show in New York and had been fascinated by the new things he was doing. Thirty years ago we had loafed around together in Stanley Rose's bookshop in Hollywood and had gone to some of the Friday night fights there, and had talked, and now look at us.

Permission to enter and eat was suddenly granted, the mother and daughter had already had supper, so my cousin and I were obliged to go in, and although I hoped I might be able to speak with her again, I didn't imagine it would be likely. I had had at least a hundred thousand interrupted chats with pleasant people in different places which I had always hoped might be continued and possibly even concluded, but not one of them *had* been, although they had been continued in chats with other people, but never concluded, not even at the time of the first divorce, and not even at the time of the second.

There just isn't any concluding of the talk between people, married, divorced, friends, enemies, strangers, or people with their names and addresses in a book or on a special piece of paper. This loss is never unbearable.

What has one ever said to anybody that in the end hasn't been painful to recall because it hasn't been *anything?* Who can regret the interruption of his own useless talk, since it is always about himself, always inept, always larded over with the best of it for himself, always a lie that announces itself as a lie in the very texture and tone of it, with only laughter in the speech letting the other know, 'This is a lie, disbelieve it if you like, if you can, if you dare, for if I can say it is a lie, as I *am* saying, and mean it, as I do, is it not true then that my *saying* that it's a lie may *also* be a lie?' Believe me, if all those endearing young charms that I saw in truth's own young eye, and heard in her own merry voice are lies, need *any* truth be true? Can false be false which in the eye is youth and unbeholden to either false or true, or in the voice tolls a better order than either or both, the order of the first, the living self, as in, for instance, the silent, smiling, watching middle girl—'Ye gods, who is this fast-talking, ridiculous-looking, pushcart-peddling, sorrow-laughing, father-looking, moustache-brushing, all-loving nut? Does mother actually *know* him? Is he actually somebody? Ye gods,' as the Mayor's daughter in *The Music Man* said.

And there she was again with her father, after the radio broadcast of the Las Vegas fight. And then along came her mother and her sisters, and so, for once in my life, interrupted talk, which in the past had always *remained* interrupted, was now picked up: "In those days Fletcher Martin was just starting out, and as for me, although I had been working at it for years, there was really no telling if my writing would ever be given the stamp of approval. At the Postal Telegraph office in Fresno where I worked as a messenger there was a red-ink pad and various stamps which a delivery clerk used upon the envelope of a telegram after he had sealed it: RUSH, REPLY REQUESTED, COLLECT, LEAVE UNDER DOOR, or simply SEND SOME-BODY A TELEGRAM. On the nightshift there was a one-armed messenger who wrote poems, and always took a new poem to the delivery clerk's desk, picked up a stamp, banged it down on the bottom of the new poem, and said, 'This poem has been given the stamp of approval by the man who wrote it, Ed Everhart.'"

"Whatever happened to Ed Everhart?" my cousin said.

"You keep out of this. It hasn't got anything to do with Ed Everhart. This is my cousin, John Saroyan. As it happens, Ed Everhart got married. Beef gets the stamp of approval, as we know, of the U.S. Department of Agriculture, and so does everything else. It doesn't matter who does the approving or what the meaning of the approval is, the important thing is that it's there, and at that time, in the depression, Fletcher Martin's painting and my writing hadn't been given the stamp of approval. What do you do, what is your work?" I said to the father.

He told me, and I said, "I am interested in madness. I believe it is the biggest thing in the human race, and the most constant. How do you take away from a man his madness without also taking away his identity? Are we sure it is desirable for a man's spirit not to be at war with itself, or that it is better to be serene and ready to go to dinner than to be excited and unwilling to stop for a cup of coffee, even? Also, how long is madness *ever* total? A minute? Five minutes? I have known *total* madness—during the War—during which two things were troublesome possibilities—murder and suicide—but even while the madness was total, and even while these two things were possibilities, even while I felt deathly, raging, useless, hating, forsaken, alone, beyond help, I was still aware, inter-

94

ested, watchful, and myself, the one who is addicted to finding the absurdity and hence the comedy in anything, including himself and *his* way, his ways, especially those ways which have excess in and to them, and therefore fraudulence, the ways of madness, for instance. I was in pain but the pain was laughable, swinging a sharp knife around my head and at my eyes. I was in sick pain that prayed God to come out and wrestle like a man, it's *your* pain, not mine, come out and wrestle for it, you don't want me to go talking to some stupid Army psychiatrist, do you?"

"That fast talk," I said to the man, "was fast because I wanted to get it out of the way as quickly as possible, but didn't want to cut any of it, because if I did, you might not get the picture of the madness I knew in London during the War. Man's madness is man, himself. If man becomes too much for himself, if his madness becomes too much to put up with, to wait with, alone, what is the good of running to Freud instead of to God? Instead of running to the *source* of the whole thing, the source of the man himself, and the madness itself? Those who are uncontrollable from pain can be helped a moment by Freuds and Oslers, and of course they should be, but what is the good of believing that that small desperate help is also the way to heal the whole thing, the man's own self, his own truth, terrible or lucky or both by turns, or simultaneously? During the madness I hurt no one, made no disturbance, went to no doctor, said good morning to those I knew who said it to me, worked—that is, wrote, *tried* to write—and after three days and three nights of wrestling became tolerable again to myself, as my madness was again tolerable to itself, to me, to the human being, the human race. This is impersonal. I am not implying that I accomplished something cool—it *was* hell, as hell can only be known by those who are there *while* they are there. The most and the best that I have ever learned I learned during that madness, and I know I could not possibly have learned it any other way. I don't like the useless, and that madness *was* useless, it was total, it was killing, it was hell, and my hatred of it was raging, and then, without changing the truth of any of this, wrestling the uselessness, wrestling God, if you will, wrestling the source, after three days—but I may not be accurate here, it may have been after three crucial minutes somewhere along the line, or even only three seconds, we're swift, we're diabolically swift and clever—all, all, absolutely all of it, all that had been useless was now useful, supremely useful, and I was there, shot and all atremble inside, eager to seize this new and unexpected means by which to know something more, to learn something more. I guessed then, and I guess now, that madnesses of all kinds in men of all kinds have been similarly healed, if I may use that word, too, and has similarly brought to each man, and to the human race, its deepest wisdom, long before Freud, its deepest compassion, and perhaps its only love—that is, love for the unlovable, the ugly, broken, diseased, helpless, hopeless, monstrous, criminal, crooked, and evil—all *words* of course, which the love which comes from madness can permit itself to say but is not permitted to believe, since the madness which taught the love was in its time, in that man, *each* of those things. Do we know anything about madness at all?"

"Well," the man said, "we certainly know it's better to put up with ourselves than not to. Some people can't. No, I really don't believe we know too much about madness, or what to do about it. Running to the psychiatrist is something else again entirely—that's only some kind of fun for some kind of people—lazy people, I suppose. And a lot of people are turning themselves over to public mental homes, or private ones, and that's something else again, too. In which of the following three men is the regression most extreme? The man who goes to a bar, the man who goes to a woman, or the man who goes to a psychiatrist?"

"The man who goes to a psychiatrist, of course."

"You'd be surprised how many people believe it's the man who goes to a bar, and how few understand that running to a psychiatrist is actually *infantalism,* except when it's exhibitionism, and then it's comic. Well, it looks like we're in."

"It's great to arrive."

In ten minutes the limousine was off the boat, rolling through the bright streets of Menominee, which has always been my destination after madness.

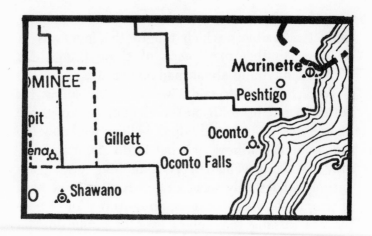

11.

Night-driving is another thing, especially West to the great open lands, especially over a highway with little or no traffic.

To begin with, it's *extra* driving. In order to *be* night-driving, the driving must take place *after* the driver has driven more than enough, after he has known deep tiredness, has forgotten it, and is now exhilarated, and must go on. It isn't simply driving at night, it is going on, possibly foolishly, to find out what's out there *now*, not so much along the highway, in the terrain, under the sky, but in the interior geography of the driver himself. Is he driving out into his sleep, wide-awake? Into the sleep of the land? Moving in silence with the sleeping rivers moving, companionate with all sleeping, and all sleepless? Into the sleep within the sleep of the old time, the time of the generations of the animals alone, moving into, through, and out of their cycles of coming, hunting, having, eating, begating, hiding, and going, suddenly caught by the *other* hunter, the unknown stalker, there goes my soul? The creatures of fang, tooth, talon, paw, tail, and jaw, waiting to catch or be caught but never knowing which it is to be?

In the bright lights of Menominee my cousin said, "This looks like a pretty good place to stop."

"Are you mad?"

"Where to, then? South to Green Bay? Oshkosh? Sheboygan? Fond du Lac?"

"Don't stop."

"Do you want to go as far south as Milwaukee?"

"No, I just want to hear the names. We want Highway 41, is that right?"

"Highway 41, south, unless we want to go north to Stephenson and Powers."

"Lousy names. They're better south. What's first, south?"

"Marinette, about ten miles if we ever find 41. Do you want to drive all night?"

"Possibly. If you're tired, climb over to the back seat and go to sleep."

"No, I'll stay awake, too. Do you want me to drive?"

"You don't know *how*."

"I've been driving since I was a kid."

"You don't know how to drive *this* car. This is a car only I know how to drive. On a short errand of some kind in broad daylight, somebody else might be *permitted* to drive it, otherwise only I can drive it. On a night like this, on the west shore of Lake Michigan, it would be unthinkable that anybody else would drive it. Where would I be?"

"Are you identifying yourself with the car?"

"I *am*. I was identifying myself with the car while the salesman was showing it to me, although I don't remember having felt at the time that I was. But I was. I have got to identify with everything that becomes a part of my life. No sign of a sign yet?"

"Let's ask this guy at the stop light."

"Straight ahead," the man said. "Follow me, I'll show you the way."

After doing so, he waved.

"Forty one," my cousin said.

"Farewell, then, to Menominee."

"What kind of a name is that?"

"Indian."

"How do you know?"

"That's the way they talk. A Blackfoot Indian comes in at election time and says, 'Me nominee.' He wants to be Governor. We'll see a full-blooded Indian President of the United States some day."

"We'll see a full-blooded woman President *sooner*."

"I look forward to our first Negro President. In the race for Presidents, we broke the four-minute mile with a Catholic. The way is now clear for the others, one by one. I want to see an Armenian President. Azhderian, for instance."

"Who's *he*?"

"I don't know, but President Azhderian has a nice sound to it. I guess it's the *Pres* of it and the *Azh* making a kind of appropriate buzzing sound."

"What about his first name?"

"Hamazasp, I suppose. President Hamazasp Azhderian. Buzz buzz buzz. Nobody would be able to say it, with the possible exception of David Brinkley, and hasn't *he* got himself a name?"

"What's the matter with Chet Huntley?"

"Nothing at all. Huntley's away out there, and there's something about Chet I can only suggest by saying it's Chet. President Hamazasp Azhderian, that's the man I'm waiting to see in office. I'd like the order to be about like this, for purposes of equity. After the Catholic, a Jew. Then, a twice-married, twice-divorced beautiful woman, known to be fond of bed and gazoomp. Then, a Negro, preferably *very* black. Then, a full-blooded Blackfoot. And finally Hamazasp Azhderian. What's *this* town?

"Marinette."

"What's the river we just crossed?"

"Menominee. We're in Wisconsin now."

"A lot of Armenians settled in Wisconsin, mainly around Racine, I believe. Maybe that's where we'll find our boy, Ham. During Lincoln's administration we had a fellow from somewhere around here—Illinois, maybe—called Black Tom Corwin. What's our highway west?"

"Well, out of Marinette, it's 64, but it's a very thin line on the map. If we want to pickup a great highway, we've got to go down to Green Bay."

"We don't want to. How thin a line on the map is it?"

"You can hardly see it."

"That'll be a two-lane highway, and just right

101

for a night like this. Almost no traffic at all at this hour, most likely, and you know what that means?"

"You'll fall asleep at the wheel."

"No. We'll see a deer, maybe. An owl or two. A few rabbits. Maybe a possum or a groundhog or whatever those slow-moving head-thoughtfully-down animals are. You think I'm half-asleep *now,* don't you?"

"You've been driving about thirty miles an hour."

"I'm getting used to the night, which happens to be a night I happen to like very much. Here's Highway 64, so what's the first town that's likely to have an all-night cafe?"

"Antigo."

"Good name. How far west is it?"

"It was on the sign there just a moment ago."

"Well, how many miles did the sign say?"

"I didn't notice."

"O.K., from the map, what's it *look* like?"

"About a hundred and fifty miles. It's a little after midnight now. A hundred and fifty miles at an average of twenty-five miles an hour is six hours, if we don't stop on the way, and if we do, we'll be getting in there around half past seven in the morning."

"This is a *proper* highway for night-driving. Two narrow lanes, no traffic, Wisconsin, going west, and the night. The thing that was good about Black Tom was that he had been born in Armenia—in Bitlis, I hope. He spoke with an accent. He had a great sense of humor. And he was honest. There was a war, and an annexation of a great part of

Mexico by Texas, and he was the only man in the Senate who spoke up for the Mexicans. Keep your eye open for the night-watchers, I think you'll see something, and if you do and I don't happen to be looking in that direction, let me know, because I want to see it, too. I want to see everything I possibly can on this drive to Antigo."

"Here comes a car."

"I can *see the* car."

"Is there room enough for two cars on this narrow highway?"

"Let me know if you see a thoughtful animal."

"There *was* room, but it was close. We don't have this kind of countryside in California."

"It isn't the countryside we don't have, it's the kind of tree and foliage, bush and bough, brook, pond, and lake. The grasses here stay green through the summer. Ours dry to a brittle brown. This is the kind of country the animals love, and this is the hour at which their thoughtfulness is most reverent and enchanted. What about *after* Antigo? What's the next big town?"

"On 64 it's Merrill. Isn't Antigo far enough?"

"I'm not sure. This is a hell of a night. I don't want to leave it just to go to sleep. This is *better* than sleep, and not especially unlike it, when sleep is at its best."

"We're not following the Triptik any more, in case you don't know."

"I know. A Triptik is not a religion. O.K., look there."

"Oh, boy, a deer."

"I love them. Their beauty scares me. You **saw** the way he moved. It scares me to see so much **mute** magnificence in one creature. Pains me."

"The hunting and shooting of them is one of **the** great American pasttimes."

"I won't knock the hunters. They're looking for meat. In a monument of quivering perfection, they're looking for hamburgers."

"Is that story about when you went deer-hunting with Stanley Rose and Nathanael West true?"

"What story?"

"The way I heard it, the three of you finally came face to face with a great buck just standing there, looking right at you, and you were supposed to shoot, but you just stood and looked, so finally one of them whispered, 'For God's sake, shoot.' And you said, 'Shoot *him*—don't be ridiculous, it would be like shooting my father.' Did that happen, or anything like it?"

"No, but I used to drive with Stanley now and then from Hollywood to Mexicali, generally starting out at one or two in the morning, after we had been drinking, and it was always Stanley's theory that about fifty miles south of Mexicali we'd shoot ourselves some game. Nathanael West and some of the other writers who used to hang around Stanley's bookstore in those days used to go on those hunting trips, too. In Mexicali, though, we used to stop at a bar where Stanley had a friend, Eddie Sandoval, who owned the place. We'd have a drink, and then some Mexican food and a couple of bottles of Mexican beer, and Eddie would sit and talk with us until around noon and then Stanley would ask how the hunting was, and Eddie would say it wasn't good, it wasn't worth the bother, why not get some sleep in the back room of the restaurant while he roasted a pheasant, or a rabbit, or a pigeon, or a mouse, or something. Eddie Sandoval did all that stuff so Stanley could feel he had been a sportsman and had gone hunting. He never really went hunting, he just liked to drink and drive somewhere at night. He had done Eddie Sandoval a favor of some kind—he had done a lot of people a favor—so Eddie was always glad to see him and not let him pay for anything. Old Stanley Mexicali Rose. I don't suppose you remember the song?"

"Of course I remember it. It came out just last year, didn't it?"

"No, that was the revival. The *first* Mexicali Rose came out the year my mother's kid brother Aram got married and bought the house on the northwest corner of Ventura and First, about 1922, I guess. In the house was the first pianola I ever saw in a home, not in a store, and of course I thought it was everything—youth, love, success, truth, America, laughter, the heartbreak that comes from sheer joy, the ineffable anguish of desire and ignorance. One of the rolls I heard on the pianola was Mexicali Rose. The clamor and clatter of that song on the pianola made me proud and sick—proud to be able to feel so much about so much, and sick because I couldn't figure out how to put my arms around the whole thing and hug it and have it and hold it and keep it."

"When did Stan die?"

"*Stan?* Did you know him?"

"I met him two or three times. He used to visit Mihran any time he came to Fresno."

"About ten years ago, he died. One time on our way to Mexicali I had this twenty-two pistol I liked to shoot tin-cans with. You think *this* is slow driving—Stanley *never* drove over thirty miles an hour. He didn't die in an automobile accident, he died of drink, boredom, and loneliness. We're going fifty, you know, because I want to be ready to slow down in case there's another deer to see. Well, about daybreak these tramp countryside birds started lighting on wire fences and singing—*trumpeting* might be a better way of putting it. Fat, raffish, cocky birds of some kind with piping clear voices and seven or eight words of preposterous exultation.

Of one of them Stanley said, 'Dirty little bastard, thinks he's Roosevelt.'

'Stop at the next one,' I said, 'and let me try this gun on him.'

So he stopped and I got out, and the bird changed his position on the fence-wire, so he could watch me better. I was off about ten yards, so I aimed and fired. I missed, of course, which was just fine, and the bird leaned forward a little. I mean, he didn't fly away. He just seemed interested. You know how it probably is with a bird like that: 'Who *are* these birds out here? How do *they* sing?' Stuff like that. I moved about five yards closer, but still he stood there on the fence-wire and watched. Curiosity, pure and simple. I held my arm straight out, aimed, and fired again. Nothing, and the bird's still there. Well, the hell with him, I decided to walk right up and *make* him fly away, so I did, but he didn't fly away. Now, when I held my arm out, the muzzle of the revolver almost reached him. I aimed and shot and missed again. And then the bird took a little hop on the wire to get into a better speaking position, and he spoke. It was the most audacious thing I had ever heard. There I was trying to shoot him dead, and there he was fascinated, fearless, and bursting with love. While I'd been hunting, so to put it, Stanley had had a chance to take a couple of swigs from the bottle he had in the pocket of his jacket. Now, he got out of the car to watch. I took aim again and was about to press the trigger when Stanley said, 'Don't *shoot* him, kid. Hit him over the head with the butt.' "

We didn't see another deer. We saw two owls, though, and three rabbits, two of which nearly killed themselves under the tires of the car, making me jam on the brakes. We came to Harmony Corners, Pound, Mountain, Langlade, Elton, and Polar, each of them sleeping in the holy night—Christmas isn't the holy night, or at any rate it isn't the only holy night. Any night you're driving (through your life) is a holy night.

At a little before three we came to Antigo and went to one of the three all-night cafes for coffee and doughnuts.

"How about stopping *here?*" my cousin said.

"If there's a fair motel."

The waitress told us there was, and how to get there, so we bought ourselves a pint each of strawberry ice cream, and drove there—Kasson's.

"Number nineteen," the sleepy man in the office said, "twelve dollars, just across over there, pay in the morning."

A fine room it was, too, with a fine shower—and I hadn't had one since Saturday morning at the Royalton in New York. The day was still Monday for me, although it was actually three hours along into Tuesday. After the shower I ate the pint of ice cream, remembering the deer, hearing the pianola, wondering about Black Tom Corwin, and worrying about the chances of Hamazasp Azhderian to be elected President in my life-time.

"I may have to live to be a hundred."

"What?"

"I thought you were asleep."

"Only half."

As for me, I didn't want to sleep, I wanted to think about the night I was in, and at the same time about all of my nights, because it seemed wise to do that, since I had come far into the future, had come a full half-century into it, to July 23rd, 1963, and to Antigo, in Wisconsin. I had also come to July 23rd, 1911, in Campbell, California, near San Jose, and wait a minute, if my father isn't dead, just dead, he's *dying*, and where am I, almost three years old? I'm fast asleep in that sleepless house where my father's dying, but I know nothing of dying, nothing of death, but now, fifty-two years later, in Antigo, I do. I know of *his* dying, of any man's, of my own, of any animal's, any spirit's, and knowing, and *for* knowing, I know of the reality of living as well, better than ever, and I want to think, on behalf of the dead, in their serene Antigo night.

It isn't ever where are you *now?* Everybody is in everybody forever, where else could everybody possibly fit? It has *got* to be back in that particular package which is the home of him, he fits nowhere else, alive or dead, coming to life or leaving it, being born or dying, the only destination in either direction is that body started all over again, the highway out is the highway in, a body coming out of the night is inhabited by the dead getting back into the package they need, long since dead men and women and boys and girls all together in the brandnew ancient package. But while the carrier of the body, the keeper of the graveyard-nursery in which the dead were buried and the newly-born were cradled, while the carrier moves nearer and nearer to his own night of leave-taking, racing in a limousine down the highway, or loafing upon the grasses alongside, the dead in him at birth, which *made* him, which gave him his own illusion of person, one by one leave, so that when it is at last, or all too soon, *his* time to go, they are *all* gone, and he must go alone.

At the time of my earliest writing, when I was the owner of an Underwood, the thing that stopped me cold was my ignorance of my past. I couldn't invent it, and it hadn't happened. Something had happened for thirteen years but not enough to allow me to take a line and carry it to where it had gone, where all lines go, because I myself *hadn't* gone. When will I have my past? When will there be enough of it, known to me, to permit me to know there is a form to all of it, which all men have? How can I say anything when I don't *have* and don't *know* the past?

And then all of a sudden I not only had it and knew it, there was too much of it. And instead of having what I had wanted, what I had waited for, I had what I didn't want, what I hadn't waited for, and again I couldn't write.

I was sitting on my bed in room 19 of Kasson's in Antigo, wide-awake in thought of my dead, when I realized I was fast asleep, dreaming I was wide *away*, down the highway, racing to space, away out there in the morning, ahead of the sun, going and gone in sleep, and so I swung the limousine to the side of the road among trees, into a pocket of them, and said, "Let the sun come up, then, *without* my witnessing of it. Let the light come and *not* find my eyes. If this is death, let the other lad have life."

When I got up in the morning, my cousin was bringing cartons of coffee out of a paper sack, and he said, "Did you leave your bedside light on? It was on all night. I half-woke up a couple of times and thought you were up, but it was still on when I got up and you were in bed."

As he talked and I remembered the lived truth and the sleeped truth moving together in their separate languages, I asked myself, "How did I find that place of trees beside the highway?" And I knew I had found it by sliding into the pocket of my bed, and into sleep, and into my past, and into my death wide away into the future long since gone far down the pianola highway.

110

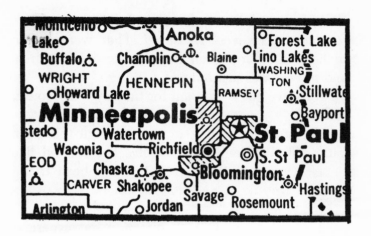

12.

The thing that was best was being free, and I had known this best thing most deeply when I had been in my own car on a long drive. I had known this freedom in myself, most memorably, most unforgettably, getting into my car, going, and not stopping until I felt like it.

In the morning in Antigo, I felt again the worth of this possession, so that the coffee I drank in room 19 of Kasson's Motel was indescribably satisfying.

The day ahead was a miracle I knew would be fulfilled.

My whole life was a lark. All of my years were in the morning cheer of expectation, because I was free. My debts had no reality. My wealth was in this moment, this freedom, this awareness of the enormity of my good luck. The hard times, trials, tribulations, agonies, doubts, stupidities, frustrations, losses, failures, fears, and follies were not forgotten, they were *treasured*. They were *known* to be part of my good luck—because I was free, and my car was just outside, waiting.

"Have we got a program for the day?" my cousin said.

"No, but we're going to pass through the Twin Cities, St. Paul and Minneapolis, because I'd like to see Tyrone Guthrie's Theatre. I've been trying to guess why he chose Minneapolis."

"Who's *he?*"

"A director, good at *all* directing but expert at crowds in action. In the world an excited crowd has a kind of reality that's impossible to keep in line, but on a stage a director has *got* to keep it in line, to make the excitement behave and be useful to his story. He'll do Shakespeare in Minneapolis of course, and he'll be at home doing Shakespeare, but he'll do American plays, too, so why Minneapolis?"

"Maybe they asked him."

"My question is answered, and let me say I'm glad I took you to your first day at Emerson School in Fresno. Were you scared?"

"I suppose so, but I really don't remember, so maybe I wasn't. How long will we be at the theatre?"

"Nothing like that. It's just that we *may* come upon it, and if we do, we may see if we can get in, and if we can, we'll study it, and if he happens to be around and isn't working or anything, I'll say hello. Otherwise, what it comes to is that Minneapolis is on the way anyway, it's west, and as I'm going west, why go north to Duluth or south to Des Moines? On the way I can think about Tyrone Guthrie's Theatre, as well as the theatre in general. What I mean is, when is going to the theatre *better* than noticing drama all around you all the time? If you're all set, let's hit the black leather bench in the limousine, and get out there into the drama."

We saw Wisconsin in broad daylight, and found it as real as Michigan, but with a difference. It *was* Wisconsin, and there *was* something different about it.

"I suppose the whole country has something in common, but about every hundred miles or so there *is* a change. The terrain itself changes, and the crops, weeds, grasses, and trees, and the way of the water maybe. Not to mention the people, and how they stand, and walk, and talk, and what they think they're doing."

"What *are* they doing?" my cousin said.

"Well, of course in Wisconsin some of them are making cheese, or at any rate making it possible for the cheese-makers to make cheese, but that isn't it. They're figuring it out, like Harry in *The Time of Your Life* says. And then he says, 'So what happens? My ear aches. My *ear*. What I want is a panatela cigar and a good used car, but my ear aches.' Gene Kelly away back in September of 1939, in Boston, where I was staging the thing, having taken it away from the fiasco staging it had had before I caught the first performance in New Haven, used to do that monologue so well I used to bust out laughing, even though I was at work and had the responsibility of seeing that my career as a

113

playwright didn't come to an end with my second play."

"How'd you ever learn to write plays?"

"By writing them, but you *really* learn by staging them. That's where you make or break a play. The kind of plays being *made* on the stage these days is just right for the kind of people who are working in the theatre—the self-sick, I mean, but I won't belabor this. It's just that everybody seems to forget that there could be another kind of play being made, and another kind of talent making it. For thirty years, for instance, the stuff that came out of Hollywood was accepted by great numbers of people who never suspected, didn't *need* to suspect, that the stuff was trash. There were *gradings* of this trash, and when you grade, you *grade,* period: great trash, less great, good, less good, fair, less fair, bad, less bad, terrible, less terrible, monstrous, less monstrous, unbearable, almost bearably unbearable, hideous but with good photography, and so on. What I'm talking about is *choice.* But if nobody knows enough to know there *is* a choice, then of course *that* is a fact, and there *isn't* a choice—except that there always *is,* straight up to God. God is *still* choosable. But I won't belabor *this,* either. Let Niebur do it. Between the God-lovers and the God-haters, we've had a lot of imbecility not to be sneezed at. When I was buying books for a nickel apiece in San Francisco in the late twenties and early thirties, I took home a great big book by Swedenborg one day, and the stuff was absolutely magnificent in its muddle-headedness. The poor guy kept getting more and more entangled in all kinds of inaccurate stuff he wanted to believe *was* accurate and had some kind of meaning. And it *did* of course— it meant he was mad."

"Why?"

"Well, he was humorless. How can you love God and never suspect that the equivalent of laughter in everything is at least equal to the equivalent of its opposite. How can you love God, and carry on as if laughter doesn't exit? For every groan of pain there is a roar of pleasure. I got into the theatre in the first place, writing plays, because plays were happening around me all the time—*actually* happening in stuff I saw, of which I myself was a part, or actually happening in my mind, out of memory, improvisation, exuberance, and love. That's why I'd like to see Tyrone Guthrie's Theatre—what's *he* doing about the rigidity, I mean? I'd like to see a theatre in which only the people who are *there* are the play and the players. Do you follow me?"

"That would be a saloon, wouldn't it?"

"Well, that's what it was in *The Time of Your Life,* but that isn't what I mean, now. Who is the theatre for? is what I mean. And must they *sit?* Think about it a minute. What the hell are they sitting there that way for? Are they tired, or what? Except in Shakespeare, and not even in him too often, I never heard anything on a stage that was better than stuff I have been saying all my life, and a lot of other people have been saying all theirs, too. So why do they sit there?"

"How should I know?"

"You should know because you're an Armenian, that's how. The Armenians are a people who have been *tempered* into *drama.* When they *breathe,* it's drama. It's the same with the Jews, and the Negroes. With the African Negro it isn't the same. Not that most of them didn't have a tough time and weren't consequently tempered to drama. A lot of their tempering came from nature, and the tempering that makes a people dramatic comes from other people. *Already* the Negroes have given this country more of its real culture than any other group, even *including* the Jews, who have given the country plenty; but just wait until the Negroes really set themselves free, as of course they are now at last *insisting* on doing. American culture will be out of the Negro—better, greater broader, deeper, truer, more varied, healthier, and with at least a *hope* of continuing. Nobody gave the Negro a dirty deal on *behalf* of American culture, or for the salvation of the whole nation, but that's how its turning out just the same. The survival and triumph of the despised has *got* to give God a roar of laughter. Why do they sit there?"

"Because they're sitters. Did you ever work with this fellow who has the theatre in Minneapolis?"

"No, but I was invited to a farewell party they gave for him a couple of years ago at the Phoenix Theatre where he'd just staged The *Macropolis Secret.* And once at Sardi's he and I were the guests, who after lunch were asked questions by the press. I don't know him, but they say that what he did in a play called *Tamerlane* was interesting. I didn't see it. I only go to the theatre if I'm asked, or it's mine. I don't *have* to see the plays—any of them. I especially avoid the hits, even when I'm *asked,* as

I was by the new playwright, because audiences at hits annoy me."

"Why?"

"They're *there* only because the thing *is* a hit, but what is the thing itself? You may not have known a Fresno kid called Shag Shirinian who one night in 1929 sat in the parlor at Ida's on 6th Street in San Francisco for two hours waiting for his turn with the girl who was the hit of the house; but at least *that* was for a good cause. I don't mean that Ida needed Shag's two dollars. I mean Shag needed to be kept waiting, as if for the mother of his kids. The theatre's too rigid. The plays *are*. The seats are, but most of all the *people* in the seats are. Where do we live? In the mind, of course, and the theatre *is* in the mind, but we also live in the body, and the body doesn't like to sit, it likes to stand, walk, and go through the motions of being real. What I mean is the purpose of art is to give the traveling human race an improved map that shows the way to itself. If art isn't for *that*, what is it for?"

"For nothing."

"Well, that's right, too, of course, by which I mean I'm interpreting your remark to mean that art is for the artist himself, but O.K., let it *be* for the artist himself *first*, and *then* let it be for the people. Being unhappy is no excuse for not wiping the nose, for instance. One May both wipe the nose and continue to be unhappy, if you follow." My cousin blew his nose. "There you are."

"I don't think you could get a three-act *play* out of that," he said.

"There's another thing, that business of three acts. Have you ever spent a day in three acts?"

"Three is a mystical number. Mihran says so."

"Eight's a *more* mystical number."

"It *can't* be. Six and nine *might* be, but how could eight be mystical? What is there eight *of?*"

"What is there three of?"

"The Holy Trinity, for instance."

"Did Mihran have any other examples, perhaps out of India? I know he did a lot of reading of Indian stuff. I went with him one time to the Parlor Lecture Club when I was eleven or twelve to hear this Indian Swami, Yogananda I think his name was, and the place was full of these wonderful overweight American ladies, wives and mothers, who were absolutely awe-stricken by the scorn the Swami had for them, for America, for the values of America, for the absence of spirituality in the nation, for the glorification of matter, but the man himself was a soft, brown, oily bore, that's all. If *you* had something you thought was important to everybody, as he did, would you be willing to have only a few nice fat ladies hear about it? I never could understand the Swamis who came from India to California, and died in Los Angeles, as this fellow did. So far his body hasn't deteriorated as much as other bodies do, and a number of people are making something of that, too—money, that is. Krishnamurti, on the other hand, after Annie Besant tried to get him to believe he was Jesus or somebody, kicked it *all* out—not religion, that's always at least personal—he kicked out messing around emotionally about confusion. Give me another example of *three* being mystical. Make it scientific if you can."

"At its source *life* may be three things—a substance, something else I'll *call* a non-substance, and an action."

"And a *fourth* thing could be something not known, possibly not *knowable*. Numbers are inevitable of course, into infinity. That may be the reason for the impulse to find what is called the Oneness of things—infinity's too much, the endlessness of numbers is too much, it's going too far, so there is an impulse to move back to One, but One is too few, so then Two is tried, and then Three, as with the Christians, but Three is actually both too few and too many—and at the same time as good a number as any, if it's *numbers* we want to fool around with. Eight is mine."

"Why?"

"It's got harmony. Two, four times. Two isn't bad, to begin with. Opposites, and that's one of the truest things we have, most likely, and the thing to be best understood. What good is right without wrong, for instance? The struggle, in other words, is the thing to be best understood. The contest. The choice. This—the choice—is that part of the whole thing that also needs a lot of thinking about, watching, and trying to understand. I like eight because I like the *looks* of it, to begin with. Two attached wholes, zero twice, infinity twice, infinity equally divided into *two* infinities, but the hell with it. Eight's my number because I was born in 1908, and I'm crazy about me. What's the word about Eau Claire?"

"At the confluence of the Eau Claire and Chippewa Rivers, this is a compact city of 37,987 souls. Early a logging community, Eau Claire today is industrially active."

"I like these little messages from the A. A. A., but what I really like is *going,* being *free* to go. Had I not been able to earn a living as a writer, I can't see how I could possibly have become anything that didn't give me the same freedom—the *total* freedom, I might say—that writing gives me. I have *got* to be free. Now, of course *anybody* in this country is free. If he's got a job he can't abide, he can quit. If he's captured by other things and can't get out of them, he's got his car. And I've got *mine*. Why does it use so much oil?"

"Camshaft."

"What?"

"I don't know. A quart every hundred miles isn't so bad, at thirty-five cents a quart. The car's giving you twelve miles to a gallon of gas, so let it use a little extra oil."

"Could the block be busted?"

"If it is, it couldn't possibly be *badly* busted because when the block is badly busted you don't cruise at seventy miles an hour and pickup to eighty any time you need to. You've got a great car. The problem is who is F. B. N., and why did he drive the car so little?"

"I'd like to get to the bottom of that all right."

When we came to St. Paul my cousin read, "Capital of the state, it is noted for its fine residential sections. With thirty lakes within thirty minutes and 88 parks, St. Paul has exceptional recreational facilities. Population 313,411."

"How about Minneapolis?"

"Population 482,872, Minneapolis is famed for its flour mills and linseed products. It is the largest distributing center in the country for tractors and agricultural implements. The University of Minnesota, Augsburg College and Seminary (Lutheran), MacPhail College of Music, Minneapolis College of Music, and Minnesota College of Law, Walker Art Center, and Minneapolis Institute of Art are here."

"Oh, boy."

"Corny?"

"No, that sentence. Now, let's see if we can ask somebody to tell us how to get to Tyrone Guthrie's Theatre."

"This is St Paul, let's *get* to Minneapolis first."

"Let's have it in mind."

On the open highway later, I remembered that the traffic in St. Paul and in Minneapolis, as well as the hunt for Tyrone Guthrie's Theatre, had slowed down the driving, for it had been in the early afternoon, and already a lot of work-shifts were over and workers were headed for home in Cadillacs, Buicks, Chryslers, Chevrolets, and now and then a Mercedes-Benz, or a Porsch. I didn't see a Rolls Royce, though.

In a cross-country drive a man at the wheel of a car can find himself becoming annoyed by city traffic, by stop lights, by racing to beat them, or to be first in line for the change to green, and this

121

annoyance is dangerous. This doesn't necessarily mean that the annoyance is dangerous in that it can be the cause of an accident: in city traffic at home-going time everybody avoids an accident every fifteen or twenty seconds, in any case. The annoyance is dangerous in that it makes the avoidance of an accident a strain. It wears out the driver and makes him believe that people going home in cars are bores. I was an annoyed driver in Minneapolis until I saw an even more annoyed driver pass me with so much contempt for having taken three-fifths of a second in which to take off instead of one-fifth, that as he passed he gave me the pitying look I had a moment ago given another slow-starter—a nun who shamed me with the serene calm of her scrubbed rosy face. The pitying look was so ridiculous I had to laugh, and then take it easy.

It is easy to take it easy, no matter what kind of traffic you are driving in. All you do is relax comfortably and know that even if you win the Grand Prize, your net profit in terms of time saved will be three minutes. After that, I actually *enjoyed* being in the traffic.

An annoyed driver goes blind to everything excepting that which is related to the race he's racing. I hadn't gone to St. Paul and Minneapolis *solely* to hunt for Tyrone Guthrie's Theatre, I had been routed through the Twin Cities by the A.A.A., and it may be that there *was* no other route to take. That situation still holds for quite a few large cities, but it isn't likely to hold very much longer. If the afternoon is hot, and there is a glaring sun, impatience and annoyance are likely to *sneak* up on a driver. Stopping for a cup of coffee and a change of pace is a good idea, but the problem is better resolved within the driver himself.

All over the country there are kids in cars who like to express themselves by their jazzy driving. In Minneapolis one of these boys in a very old highly-polished black Chevrolet with rear tires larger than the front ones came racing alongside to invite me to race. We were going better than sixty miles an hour when we had to draw up at a light, and during the wait the boy got set. When the light changed he shot out expecting me to shoot out, too, and inasmuch as I didn't, he slowed down until he sat in his car straight across from me, both cars traveling around thirty miles an hour.

"Come on, let's race," he said.

"If you know where the Tyrone Guthrie Theatre is, I'll follow you."

Even though he'd never heard of it, he wanted to be helpful, in appreciation of the fact that he hadn't been taken for a nuisance. "I got to go, but ask a cop," and off he went like a shot.

Getting out of Minneapolis took time, but it was worth it, and I *had* time. I had as much time as I *cared* to have, because I was free in the first place, and then I had become free of annoyance. There is no real freedom for the man who is in so much of a hurry that he is annoyed by the human race and by the hot glaring afternoon sun.

In the outskirts of Minneapolis, near Saint Bonifacius, two new cars were on the side of the highway, among weeds. One of them was on its back, like a bug, the other was smashed. The drivers and passengers were on their feet, but they were hurt. Three cops and a dozen people standing around with the three men and two women who were hurt made it a complete picture. That is to say, a complete picture of that which should not have happened. One could only rejoice that there were no kids involved and that none of the others were on their backs.

"What happened?" my cousin said.

"Personality-failure. An accident is almost always the consequence of a flaw of personality—at least on *one* side, but generally on both. I have got to meet my flaws as they present themselves to me, because if I don't, and if I don't recognize the flaws *as* flaws, I'm bound to make a mistake, and a mistake while driving a car is a serious matter."

As the hotrod boy had suggested, we'd asked a cop if he could tell us how to get to the Tyrone Guthrie Theatre, and then we'd asked a man in a car, a boy with a girl in the street, but nobody knew what we were talking about, although several of them told us to go to Ackerman Drive and turn left, but only trying to *find* Ackerman Drive had gotten us lost, so we had finally stopped looking.

We had driven out into Minnesota, the land of Olsen and Johnson, and a lot of other Swedes and Norwegians.

Along Highway 7 we saw a lot of pheasants, and just before dark we reached Cosmos, where we stopped for gas, oil, coffee, and a brief chat with a waitress.

"How did this town come to be called Cosmos?"

"I don't know."

Across the street from the coffee shop, where we bought a pint each of strawberry ice cream, there was a blacksmith, but he did machine-work, mainly.

We ate the ice cream in the cool of the evening, driving slowly from Cosmos to Watertown, where we expected to stop at a Motel with a high A.A.A. rating, but we were dreaming. If you want a room at a Motel in the summertime you've got to get there early in the afternoon. You can't just drop by any time you feel like it and expect to find a room. Motels are no longer for the convenience of motorists, they're big business, and they attract the same kind of people the big hotels used to attract—people who want to stop at a good place because they never have. Even the door to the Desk of this Motel was locked, and the girl behind the Desk took her time about unlocking it. She was amazed that I didn't know they didn't have a room, but I didn't, and for a moment I expected to be asked if I didn't know there was a war going on.

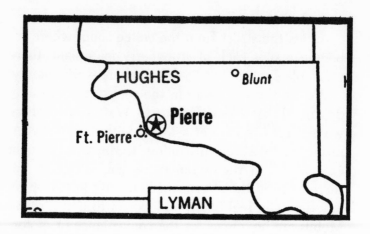

13.

In Watertown there was a small hotel, built in 1898. My cousin went into the place to find out if there was a room. While he was gone it seemed to me I might work on a new song: *What a Town is Watertown*. But before I could so much as *think* about a second line, two old gents who were also from around 1898, or 63 years of age each, dropped by the double-parked car to chat—about New York, at first, because they had seen the license plate, and then with a little urging from me about Watertown, just across the Minnesota border into South Dakota: "Good hunting around here, pheasant especially." And then about the hotel: "Oh, they've got rooms all right, they've *always* got rooms, but I don't think the rooms have been much good since along about 1908." Was Pop a wit, or had something happened in 1908? Before I could find out my cousin came back, all smiles, and he said, "He's got one room with four beds in it, but without a wash basin, and one room with only three beds in it, but *with* a wash basin. We can have our choice at four dollars for the night. Which one do you think we ought to take?"

"Get in."

"Aren't we going to spend the night?"

"We're going to spend the night, but not here. We're going to have a hamburger, because we're in South Dakota, but *just* in, and I want to know South Dakota at night, at least a little."

He got in and I said so long to the old gents, and we drove off.

"When are we going to have the hamburger?"

"How about right now, at this place with all the cars around it?"

"O.K."

Well, the thing about hamburgers is that even though the ground-meat is never much good the finished sandwich itself with all the trimmings invariably tastes just right. With coffee, it is the kind of American thing that can't happen anywhere else in the world. At the Drug Store on the Champs Elysees in Paris, for instance, a hamburger is so meaningless that I have had to force myself to take a second bite, all the while feeling America has been betrayed, perhaps by me, for trying to eat the thing, or by France for making it. A true hamburger *is* America. Eating it is participating in a folk rite. One always wants a second one, but seldom has it. Three cups of coffee, and I was ready for South Dakota, and so was my cousin, who only fifteen minutes ago had really wanted to stop. We took off on Highway 212 headed for Redfield, seventy-two miles down the road. We soon heard thunder and saw great bolts of lightning at the edge of the horizon. The car was dusty and smeared with insects, so I hoped for rain. At the same time the air was hot and humid.

"Will it rain?" I said.

"It *might*, but if it does, it will be for only a minute. Have you ever seen lightning like this before?"

"No, this is like having a box seat at a Fourth of July celebration. I've never seen lightning make so much light, either—fire-color, purple, red, and maybe a little blue. And double flashes, not single. Double, like the second surprise in fireworks, after which everybody says, 'Aaaaaaah.' What seems to be the trouble? Meteorologically, that is?"

"Hot air clashing with cold air is all it is."

"In that case, in South Dakota the difference is made by the fact that the hot air is very hot and the cold air is very cold, so that the thunder is louder, longer, crisper, more varied, and the lightning is bigger and brighter and more prolonged. Would you say that that's along the lines of fact, or would you be willing, as I am, to believe the thunder and lightning are the consequence of the fact that the Indian Gods are annoyed with somebody about something."

"The situation *has* its Indian aspects," my cousin said.

"It would be very interesting some day if the universe turned out to be held together and kept in operation by the various Gods who had previously been considered the inventions of simple superstitious people. It is certainly always in order for science to be patient about anything people believe, because something true about something *else* may come of it, and that's always a good thing, too."

No rain fell, but the thunder and the lightning remained on the horizon all the way to Redfield, where the Motels again had no rooms, even the ones with poor ratings, so we moved along to Highmore, where we stopped for gas and a chat with the pump-boy and his friend who drove a tractor for a living.

"What about this thunder and lightning?"

"We have a lot of it every night about this time of year."

"What about the millions of insects in the air, and the bugs I see crawling all over the cement of this station?"

"We have a lot of *them,* too."

"Why?"

"That's the way it is out here. What kind of a car is this?" I told him the little I knew. "Does it run all right?"

"Better than any car I've ever driven."

We drove on, and came at length to Pierre, about which my cousin read: "Population 10,088, the approximate geographical center of the state, it is also the capital. A lead plate, found in 1913, claimed the area for France. It had been buried in 1743 by Sieur de la Verendrye. Much of the history of the early fur trade centers around Fort Pierre, where trading posts were established in the early 19th century. Opposite the State Capitol is the Soldiers' and Sailors' Monument, dedicated to South Dakota's service men who lost their lives in World War I. 2226."

"What do you mean 2226?"

"Well, it's *there*, that's all."

"Do you know what 2226 is—to me?"

"No."

"A magic number, because it's the address of the house on San Benito Avenue I lived in for a number of very important years of my boyhood. It's even in my first play, *My Heart's in the Highlands*. I feel very good about this."

"Maybe it means we'll be back in Fresno before we know it, and we'll find Mihran his old self again. Here's the Holiday Inn, and about time, too. It's half past twelve. They'll have a room, won't they?"

"Well, we'll certainly go in and find out."

We did, and there was no room, but the boy phoned somebody and sent us to The Frontier Motel, in Fort Pierre. We paid in advance before seeing the room, and went in. It was supposed to be air-conditioned but really wasn't. The shower half-worked, and then I had a quart of strawberry ice cream, hit the sack, and heard Indians whooping up a request for rain from their Gods.

*

Three days later in Fresno we drove past the place where the house at 2226 San Benito Avenue had been, and then out Blackstone Boulevard to 1239 Swift Street where we found Mihran in the garden standing under one of the almond trees he had planted twenty or thirty years ago. When he turned to make sure who it was, a very young man was suddenly a very old man, something funny happened to all of the years, everybody talked at the same time, and then we went for a short drive while the sun was still up.